Sojourn

Sojourn

Edited by Zhana

A Methuen Paperback

A Methuen Paperback

SOJOURN

First published in Great Britain 1988
by Methuen London
Michelin House,
81 Fulham Road, London SW3 6RB

Photoset by Rowland Phototypesetting Ltd
Bury St Edmunds, Suffolk
Printed and bound in Great Britain
by Cox and Wyman Ltd, Reading, Berks.

British Library Cataloguing in Publication Data
Sojourn.
1. Fiction in English. Women writers, 1945–
Anthologies
I. Zhana
823'.914'08

ISBN 0-413-16440-3

This book is dedicated
to my grandmother,
Mrs Ophelia D. Lyle

Contents

Acknowledgements

Thanks to all the contributors. Special thanks to Najma, for loving me, to Isha, for her support and friendship, to Meiling for keeping me serious about my writing.

Thanks to God and the universe for lovingly supporting me.

Thanks to Roz for her love, and for help with the resources list.

Thanks to Pat Agana for her help and good ideas.

Thanks to my parents and my sister Anne for all their good examples.

Thanks to Pam for Rebirthing me through the process of giving life to this book.

Thanks to Pete for all his love, support, and friendship, for being there through everything, and for believing in me.

Introduction

This book has been a process of normalization for us, the Black women who brought it into being. A process of realizing that we are not freaks, that we are not the only ones, that our experience is truly shared.

One reason it was important to me to compile *Sojourn* was that the topics within have rarely been touched on before in print. Much has been written about relationships between Black men and women and between Black and white women but relationships between and among Black women are rarely described and even more rarely discussed.

We have made a start. *Sojourn* marks but the beginning of a long journey to be made.

The central questions of this book are: what is the nature of Black British culture? How can we define it? What are its cultural norms, and what are our roles as Black women in it?

Black people have, of course, lived in Britain since recorded history. The very name of Scotland comes from Scota, the African princess who founded the country in ancient times. The Celts, who are held up as being the purest of British cultures, are descended from Africans. Black communities have existed in large trading ports such as Liverpool, Cardiff and Bristol since the time of the slave trade. So, why does Britain have such an overwhelmingly white, racist consciousness?

It is impossible to talk about the Black presence in the British Isles in isolation. Discussion of our presence here immediately brings up issues of the slave trade and colonization. When writing about the community of Black British women, it is essential to do so in the context of other countries, the wider community of the Black diaspora. Black women in Britain still identify themselves as Westindian, Afro-Caribbean, African or Asian, and often still speak their mother tongue (mother's tongue?). Although they do not see themselves as being strangers or outsiders here, they maintain strong links with Black countries and many, although they were not born in Africa, have moved to African countries, or plan or hope to do so at some point in the future.

It is impossible to write about the current or historical aspects of Black British society without discussing our countries of origin, because virtually all of us see ourselves as having originated elsewhere, which perception naturally influences the decisions and actions we take here.

'We are here because you were there' is not an entirely accurate statement. It is much more accurate to say, 'We have always been here because you decided to make there part of here.'

During the time of the British Empire, whole Black nations were part of that Empire. In their own countries, Africans, Asians, and Afro-Caribbeans lived *in Britain* – under British rule. Their behaviour was British by law. Their social norms, the fabric of their culture were subject to British domination.

It is hardly surprising that Black British people who answered the call of their Motherland in the 1950s brought their culture with them. Their music, their dance, their Carnival, their patois; they had created and enjoyed these cultural forms for generations while being assured that they were, indeed, British, that England was their mother country. On their arrival, they were told that they had to drop these things – these cultural practices were 'un-British' and had to be given up in order that one might 'fit in' with British society at large. And so the great internal struggle began.

Another reason it was important to me to compile a book about relationships between Black women was because I want to get to a place where we are our own point of reference, where we form our own collective subconscious, where we set our own terms.

This book is about the lives of some Black women in Britain. Our relationships with each other and our creation of the world and our lives within it. Our self-expression, communication, recording of our own lives. Our survival.

I have concentrated on some of the relationships which are fundamental to Black women's understanding of ourselves. Mother/daughter relationships: our mothers are our first lovers, the first people we meet, our first friends and enemies. They introduce us to the world. They imprint their personalities on our minds and their views of the world on our eyes. What we know about Black women, including ourselves, we learn first from them.

Like us, our mothers have a vagina, breasts and a uterus – they have periods, and, like some of us, they have slept with men.

They more likely than not resemble us. When we look in the mirror, we see traces of a mother's face looking back at us. A nose, a chin, a tooth, a set of the jaw. A skin-shade of brown, a curl of hair, a roundness of hip, a fullness of breast.

Multiple layers of contradictions confront a Black woman who raises daughters in British society. There are the contradictions of the role of women, a role which the mother may well undervalue yet must pass on, must train her daughters for. There are the intergenerational conflicts of wanting a better life for her daughters than she had for herself, perhaps of wanting to avoid her own mother's mistakes, yet, at the same time resenting the opportunities available to her daughters, and for which she had to make sacrifices. The early migrant of the 1950s lived almost in a cultural vacuum. She usually did not have her mother, her aunties or even her sisters with her to provide role models for her children. Much has been written about the pain of isolation experienced by young Westindian mothers who found themselves cut off from their traditional extended family networks of support, about the demands of childcare which forced many women to leave their children with childminders of dubious ability and attentiveness, or else to work odd and demanding shifts in order to be home when the children needed them.

But as women are the carriers and transmitters of culture, she lost out on more than childcare and companionship. She lost out on the reinforcement of her culture in the form of having other women around who showed her how to fasten a nappy, who cooked certain foods, who spoke a certain way, who remembered a particular story or figure of speech. So, for example, in the Caribbean and in Africa, it is quite common to slip sayings and parables into conversation. A young woman might remember some of the sayings used by her mother and her granny and others back home but not all of them and, not hearing them used in common currency, she would naturally forget some. Her children would not learn as many sayings from her and, not having the trait reinforced by input from others in their environment, would come to know hardly any. Thus another feature of Black culture slips away from us and is forgotten.

Added to this is the fact that the mother might well herself feel ashamed of aspects of her culture. She might feel that her Caribbean or African accent holds her back and not want her children to pick it up, for fear it will limit or prevent their advancement. She might well, therefore, encourage the exclusive use of standard English at home and even forbid the speaking of patois or of African localized English.

A Black woman who believes that her Blackness stands in the way of career advancement and material security will encourage her children to reject that very Blackness. This can and, in the past, often did go to the extreme of even choosing a lighter-skinned partner or encouraging one's children to do so, as light skin was equated with power.

A Black woman comes to Britain where, although she considers herself British, she is immediately made to know that she is unwelcome. She may feel very homesick and begin to reject the white Western cultural norm which allows her, a human being, to be discarded as a piece of trash. She may want to reclaim, and transmit to her children, something of the culture she holds dear, which reared and nourished her. On the other hand, she might see that very culture as a stumbling block, and strive to eradicate all possible traces of it from her life and her children's consciousness. British rascism produced both reactions in Black women.

We internalized the inherent contradictions in this dilemma, and we are still playing out these contradictions today.

And what of women who don't have mothers, whose mothers were not there for us, at least not in the ways we wanted? Isha McKenzie-Mavinga's moving short story, 'Grassroots Mother Daughter', deals with the dilemma of a woman who is brought up in care by white women and then does not know how to accomplish the task of mothering her own daughters – but she still manages to do it. She feels something is missing, but she doesn't know what.

Also apt to feel something is missing are women who were separated from their mothers or from their mother countries at an early age. Iiola Ashundie's piece, 'Mother of Mine', evokes the joy of memories of the Caribbean, and of returning to the place of one's youth.

The choice of whether or not to become a mother must also be addressed, and Tod Perkins's piece, 'The Decision', examines this issue.

There are as many mothers who let their daughters down in some way, who fell short of their duties as 'mothers' as their daughters defined them, as there are mothers and daughters. It could be through harsh criticism, which destroyed budding confidence and eroded young women's self-esteem; it could be through not protecting them from the racism of schools or the police; it could be through failing to protect them physically from brutal men who raped them or, as in the case of Tyra Henry, murdered them. Black mothers are Black women who do not always makes choices which are acceptable or life-enchancing or, in some cases, even life-sustaining, to Black daughters, who are also Black women. My piece, 'Mother/Daughter', and my poem, 'For Tyra', look at Black women who could not protect, or even love, daughters who were so much like themselves because they didn't always love themselves.

Sisters – what are sisters? People with whom we begin to work out the rules for the game of life. People who have to obey the same laws as we do – those laid down by our parents, and determined by the external pressures on our parents. We grow up together in the same house, eating the same chicken every Sunday, walking down the same road to school. These are idealized pictures of sisterly behaviour. One or another is, in actuality, given more responsibility. One is favoured, one is scapegoated. You might be the smart one, your sister the pretty one, and so it goes. At home, the parents might make the daughter into the vessel for all their dreams. She is the one who must excel at school, who must not speak patois – with the others, less effort is exerted. The eldest has the responsibility of preparing Sunday dinner for the little ones. She becomes a surrogate mother, always expected to be mature and well-behaved, taking on a woman's responsibilities before she is ready. It might just as easily be the youngest, who, as the older siblings are seen as failures, becomes the mother's confidante or the one on whom the parents hang their hopes. She, the last to leave the nest, can be held up to the others as the example of a perfect daughter.

So, you have several Black women all living under the same roof, in the same social conditions, each defining her role as a Black woman differently, and each probably believing that she's right, that she knows what it's all about.

These women all make different choices about the directions to take with their lives.

It starts in the schoolyard. You begin to notice the differences. The other Black girls won't have anything to do with you because you can't understand their mother tongue, and they feel insulted. Or they beat you up to let you know they won't put up with your being 'stuck up' like your sister. You begin to realize that there are criteria for Black womanness. You can't just be born into it, you have to measure up.

All Black women. All from the same family. One runs away because she can't stand the beatings anymore. One gets kicked out, pregnant. One, a lesbian, has to leave her lovers at the door. One, who gets married, gets a secure job as a secretary or a PA, and never looks back. Clinging tentatively to her middle-class status, she never speaks patois in front of the kids.

The mother feels she has failed – except, perhaps, with the daughter who succeeds according to white society's terms. She cannot accept that she has brought all her daughters into the full flower of Black womanhood, with all its toughness, vulnerability, beauty and diversity. She has set herself standards she was never meant to meet, instead of looking inside herself for her terms of reference. And all the women end up looking at each other with suspicion and distrust, full in the knowledge that these women – who are nothing like them, who have completely different interests, goals and values – are also the guardians of their most deep-rooted and basic memories.

This is where it begins. All our analyses of sisterhood and what it means must go back to the family, our first encounters with other Black women – with each other. Of course, the Black family, a very powerful institution, has its other side – the warmth, the closeness, the security of knowing there will always be someone there who loves you. This is what is meant by 'sisterhood', the always being there, through thick and thin. The delight in each other, the warmth, the catching that look in the eye, knowing what each other is thinking, the smell of hair, the smoothness of skin, the firm gentleness of hands. The memory, often repeated, of blue moods, sudden anger, a shared joke, chicken and fried dumplings and rice and peas. They are all equally true, all equally valid, our definitions of sisterhood. No one Black woman, or even group of Black women, can define Black womanness, except as it means to them, and even those definitions are subject to change through the course of time.

Of course, the Black family, as has been well documented, has been subjected to inordinate stress by white society. The attempted breakup of our families during slavery time is legendary – what is less well known is how often we managed to stay together, despite the distance and the threat of capture and physical torture. We, usually the women, still managed to visit our children and husbands in the dead of night. So, too, we dealt with the British state's new strategy, that of dumping huge numbers of our children into 'care'. We continued to care for one another, to visit our sisters, take them out for the day, bring them gifts. To give them a taste of what Black family life is about – lest they forget. We coped, we carried on.

The mass migration of the 1950s brought with it another peril, that of part of the family being left behind. It wasn't meant to be forever. Black people did not intend to stay. But life was hard in the British Isles, it took much longer to scrape together a few pennies than anyone had thought, and everything cost so much. With babies coming, decisions had to be made. Often a family bought a house, so that family life could continue with some semblance of normality. And the children left behind had to stay behind. Sisters grew up and reached adulthood without ever meeting, sometimes without being aware of each other's very existence. When, as adults, you meet, you meet as strangers. And you wonder whether she resents you for having the opportunities she missed, or even for stealing her place in your parents' affections. It's equally true that a woman in London suddenly discovers she has a long-lost sister or cousin or aunt living in Birmingham. They've both been in Britain for twenty-five years, totally unbeknownst to one another.

And then they meet, and they discover how much they have in common. They discover in each other a new friend, a sister, they forge a common bond. They begin to recreate the joy and closeness of family. Of sisterhood.

The same story can have a different twist. The sister, after six or ten years of being left behind, is finally brought over. Money is found for her passage. The daily routine is disrupted, the family order changes. Who was the eldest is no longer the eldest. Who was the only child now has responsibility for the little ones. When you arrive from the Caribbean, perhaps you come to only one parent, to brothers and sisters who have a different mother or father to you. They talk funny, and make fun of your speech. They resent you for usurping their place in the family. At school, the teachers can't understand your speech, and you have problems. You become withdrawn and over-sensitive. At school and at home, you are labelled rebellious, belligerent, a 'problem'.

It doesn't matter which side of the Atlantic you were on. Whether you were here or there, you will have issues around being brought here or left behind, having sisters or brothers who were brought here or left behind. The same story in all its different permutations plays itself out again and again. And we think, nobody else has this problem, I'm the only one who feels this way. But, of course, we're not. It's all part of the complex and intricate tapestry of our sojourn in Britain.

In 1982, the author Toni Cade Bambara suggested to me that I put together an anthology on Black women in Britain, in order to provide access to publishing for women who might not otherwise have it. Since then, of course, many exciting developments have taken place in the publication of Black women's literature in this country. Shortly after meeting with Toni, I became a founding member of the Black Women's Editorial Collective, which organization worked together for some time to compile an anthology, but eventually fell apart. My task continued. I learned the hard way to take Toni Cade Bambara's good advice, and edit the book on my own. In the process, I co-founded the Black Women's Writing Workshop, which worked with Black women writers and would-be writers in London, creating a space for us to support each other in sharing our creativity. My belief is that all Black women are writers, each of us has a story to tell, and we just need the opportunity and the confidence to put our words on paper.

Working with the Black Women's Writing Workshop was very exciting and gratifying. We saw many Black women, including ourselves, begin to open up, and to understand and enjoy our own creative processes.

My work on the book continued. I did not feel confident enough to write the book on my own, and I felt that the same techniques we had used to get women to open up in the workshop could be used to generate material for *Sojourn*.

The topics I chose were things about which I felt all Black women would have something to say. No one could be intimidated by the idea of writing about something so basic as relationships with our mothers, daughters and sisters, about coming to this country, going Home to visit, or moving on.

The insights I have brought to this book are based on my own experiences and those of Black women currently living in Britain. They are drawn from my work with various Black women's organizations, as well as from oral histories and group discussions and workshops which I organized specifically for *Sojourn*.

We all make mistakes. I was never so wrong as when I discounted the powerful taboos which surround any discussion of our most intimate relationships. Slowly, painfully, we eked out words, phrases, scraps. The picture we've painted so far is by no means complete. We've still got a way to go.

You will probably find parts of the book difficult and disturbing. I do not apologize for anything written herein, nor do I, by any means, agree with everything. For example, my own definition of 'Black' is simply 'women of African heritage', no more and no less. However, I have included the experiences of Asian women in *Sojourn*. All the contributors to *Sojourn* identify ourselves as Black, and I felt it was important to represent some of the diversity of opinion and experience that contribute to the current, ongoing debate among Black women in Britain.

However, what was, and continues to be, exciting to me is the frequency with which those of us from widely divergent backgrounds report similar and parallel experiences, and those of us having enormously diverse experiences arrive at similar conclusions, albeit through different routes.

A sojourn, as I define it for the purposes of this book, implies not only a journey, but also a stay. It is much more than just a simple journey from point A to point B. So that, for instance, the experience of growing up in, say, Jamaica, looking to England as the mother country, developing British values and norms of behaviour, saving up to come here, arriving, experiencing racism and all its attendant pressures, making a decision to remain here, forming links and putting down roots, going Home for a holiday, considering retiring to Jamaica, and finally moving on to Zimbabwe, would be one single sojourn under this definition.

Writing about where we've come from and/or are going to be proved to be much easier than writing about our motherly, daughterly and sisterly experiences. Almost all of us had fond memories of our early years, or were eager to talk about our early painful trials. Our experience was truly international, and truly shared.

I love travelling. It brings a freshness to the most mundane aspects of life. Regardless of whether my experiences are good or bad, the fact that they take place in an unfamiliar setting brings to them the sense of fascination and delight which all of life should have.

I arrived in Britain in early 1982, unsure of what to expect. It could be supremely civilized and fun, as exemplified in the Big Red Bus movies and Swinging London TV series of my childhood. It could be horrific, as indicated by the previous year's events.

A year before, in January 1981, I had been stunned when, whilst I was visiting London as a tourist, the New Cross fire occurred.

Later, when I returned Home, I learned that a young man I'd known from school, who had grown up with my younger sister, was studying in London and had been arrested at about the same time I was there. He had been taken off of the tube and charged with stealing someone's handbag. The owner of the handbag was recorded as 'persons unknown', not having come forward, and the handbag, on not being produced, was recorded as 'items unknown' by the police.

These were my first two glimpses of the viciousness of British racism.

When I arrived at Heathrow, I was asked by an immigration official where I had come from. Thinking this was a stupid question, as I had just gotten off of the flight from New York's Kennedy Airport, I replied, 'New York'. He then asked me where I'd come from before that. Seeing a look of puzzlement cross my face, he then realized that I was an American, not a Westindian, and allowed me to proceed without questioning me further. Welcome to Britain.

Like most Black people, when I arrived in Britain, I was grateful to be here, grateful to be allowed to stay here. US Americans often see our country as an offshoot of Britain, a continuation of British culture, interrupted only briefly by the Revolutionary War. We see British literature as part of our heritage. Our actors and actresses often play British roles, and vice versa.

Of course, we know that English settlers named places in North America after their homes. But we don't realize how extensive that practice was. To walk in places where those settlers walked, to see vistas they saw, to sit under trees that shaded them 300 years ago – at last, one begins to understand the mentality of those who came to settle and dominate the North American continent. We begin to understand a people who could descend on and slaughter a whole race of people in their arrogance and their belief in their rightness. I can more fully appreciate, now, what they left behind, what they were running from. The cold, the harshness of the class system which could literally mean life or death for you or your children. America was truly the land of opportunity for escapees from a country where their whole life was planned out for them before they were born.

I understand, now, the instinct for survival which drove people to leave a small, cold, foggy, soggy island which, nevertheless, contained all they had ever known and loved, to strike out towards an unknown frontier. Even 300 years ago, the prospects for the average Englishman were a life which offered no hope for advancement, and a class system as brutal as it was unchallengeable, which puts ceilings on ambitions. To be offered a new country in which to make a fresh start was to be offered the Promised Land.

I now know the full context in which the Founding Fathers should be viewed. The freedoms we take for granted in the States – of speech, religion and the press – were breaking new ground then, and are unthinkable here in Britain even now, where it can be made a criminal offence even to state that you support an organization that has been labelled as terrorist, where a book such as *Spycatcher* can be 'banned'. In that context, for the US Founding Fathers, drafting the Declaration of Independence and the Bill of Rights was an action as bold and as innovative as the first step on the moon.

By the age of ten, I not only took for granted but actively despised those documents, for the hypocrisy they represented to my Black female mind. 'All men are created equal' – the fact that the man who penned those words owned hundreds of slaves including a Black mistress who was the mother of his children, and apparently saw no conflict in this, impressed me with a sense of the profound hypocrisy of the (usually white male) wielders of power who were held up to us for admiration as leaders of our society. The descendants of the Founding Fathers swelled with patriotic pride, while at the same time beating and imprisoning Black people who demanded such basic considerations as being served politely and considerately (and at all) at lunch counters; being allowed to sit where they liked on buses on which they had paid to ride; and being able to use whatever public lavatory was available. 'America the Beautiful' – the very words filled me with scorn. Its cherished freedoms did not, to my mind, even exist.

From my earliest years, I was acquainted with the history of slavery and its inherent brutalities and atrocities. I was educated by my parents at least as much as by the school system, which caused me to be very knowledgeable about this aspect of my history. In my first six years of schooling, most of my teachers were Black and I was, at times, incredulous that they repeated to us such phrases as 'Lincoln freed the slaves' and 'Columbus discovered America' without betraying the slightest consciousness of the irony of making these statements to rooms full of Black children. I resented having to participate in the daily ritual of reciting the Pledge of Allegiance to the US flag. It has been reported that American children recite the Pledge of Allegiance by rote, without understanding the meaning of the words. This was certainly not true in our case. We knew what we were saying, and the children in our class often changed the last line to 'with liberty and justice for some'.

Partly at school and partly at home, I was taught that the most brutal system of slavery in recorded history was the English system, the one which had operated on the North American continent, and under which my ancestors had suffered. At that time, I merely accepted that information, but from it I gained some residual pride that we had survived that system, along with relief that it no longer existed. It was, of course, perfectly logical to my mind that the English had instituted that system of slavery and the slave trade, since it was the English who had always been held up to us as the founders of the thirteen original states.

Although I was very aware of the history of slavery, I knew nothing about the history of British and European colonialism and imperialism in Africa, Asia and the Caribbean. I knew nothing of the brutalities hidden by the cloak of Empire. Britain was always held up to us as the ultimate in civilized society.

Meanwhile, here in Britain, the atrocities which had been committed by the British in Black countries were well documented. This was because the white British had no reason to suppress this information. Far from being a matter for shame, the systematic violent oppression of whole nations of people is regarded as part of a glorious past, the elevation of the white British through the subjection of inferior races. However, the history of slavery, with its attendant brutalities, is practically unknown here. Audiences in Britain were shocked and riveted by 'Roots', a TV series which showed aspects of slavery that were quite mundane, ordinary and even boring to US viewers. Why, then, this dichotomous collusion? Why should one aspect of white brutality to Black people be so openly acknowledged and discussed on one side of the Atlantic, only to remain a guilty secret on the other? The answer is that, for Britain, slavery was pushed away, cleaned up off the streets, quarantined to the Black countries, so that the British public would ignore, and eventually forget, that aspect of history – so that the greedy purveyors of cruelty for profit could continue beating, torturing, raping and murdering Black people, but far away, safe from public gaze.

The British knew what Britain was like. They cut their teeth on each other, they built the rigid class system which kept so many of them living out their lives in stinking holes. Although they kidded Black people that England was the land of milk and honey, they themselves knew they had consigned their working classes to a life with inadequate air, light, food, water, housing and health care. But, through that very class system, in which one class could be kept completely oblivious to how the other half of their own society lived, they were able to ignore, to forget. So the injustices and the brutalities went on. In slavery in Britain, these inequalities were too glaring, they were there for all to see, in Black and white. So they had to be cleaned up, whisked away, consigned to the Dark Continent. And whole systems of thought, whole networks of information had to be built to justify the savage treatment of Black and brown people.

These systems of thought still prevail in British society today. The myths of Black innate inferiority, stupidity, savagery and bestiality, which were initially introduced to justify the slave trade and colonialism, still permeate all aspects of British life, from immigration to housing, to the way we are treated by those who have direct power over us, including employers, social workers, health-care officials, and, perhaps most importantly, educators and the media.

Black and Asian people have lived in Britain – in British colonies, under British rule – for hundreds of years. Their behaviour, while essentially African and Asian by nature, was British by law. Their social norms, the fabric of their culture, were under British domination. They had been ignored for hundreds of years by Britain's whites. The majority of Britain's whites knew nothing of Britain's brutalities perpetrated in the colonies. Of course, certain classes had seen a glimpse of the horrifying nature of slavery in Britain. They had been allowed to beat, torture and otherwise maltreat their own slaves; their white countrymen had festered in foul prisons and in unsafe mines, factories and slums. Yet the ruling classes chose to forget, or to turn a blind eye.

The education system and the media were two invaluable tools in this process of erosion of memory. They did not question the British class system, but merely reinforced the idea that it was normal and inevitable. So, too, were slavery, and eventually colonization and imperialism, presented and accepted as normal and inevitable. These analyses, or lack of analyses, persist to this day. Just this week, a programme was aired on TV which documented the achievements of several English, Irish and Scotsmen who 'opened up' trade with, and brought religion to, different parts of Africa. At no point did this programme question the ethics of this drive for trade, let alone mention the cost in human suffering.

Black people have not forgotten that cost, nor are we likely to forget for a long time to come.

So why, then, did they travel so eagerly to Britain in their numbers in the 1940s, 1950s and 1960s? They truly believed it would be new rules. No apartheid in the mother country – that kind of behaviour was reserved for the colonies. No brutality, no inequality in jobs, education, health care and justice. They had made it at last. They were being not only *allowed*, but *encouraged* to travel to England en masse, and not in slave ships, but as free women and men. At last, they had made it, they had won the big prize. They had always known they were British, and now they were to be accepted as such.

I find it difficult to express the intensity of awe with which Black people traditionally regard education. I use the term 'education' in the sense in which it is widely used, to mean formal education pursued in an academic setting and ultimately leading to formal qualifications. Many Black people treat education as a totem, which will ritualistically shield the bearer from all manner of harm and provide, inevitably and automatically, for a materially secure and rosy future. This must be viewed in the context in which formal Western education was held up as a goal for Black and Asian people to strive towards in Africa, India and the Caribbean. Its lack was used by the whites in power as an excuse for the continued impoverishment of the majority Black and brown populations; its possession allowed one admission to the white-collar sector and its attendant material comforts. Those who held formal qualifications – particularly teachers, who could bestow or withhold gems of knowledge at will – were revered.

The gap between the rich and poor in Black and Asian societies meant, and still can mean, the difference between life and death, between being able or unable to feed your children, between seeing the doctor or suffering from an otherwise curable disease. So education, that obtainable magic wand that held the power of life and death, was pursued with blind zeal.

The magnet of education drew Black people to British shores in great numbers. At last, children from families who could not afford school fees could pursue secondary education. Adults, too, could gain nursing training they could otherwise never have afforded, and return Home a few years later as professionals, commanding respect and prestige in their society.

That was the dream for which families were prepared to sacrifice everything. Parents endured all manner of humiliation and degradation, worked at jobs which damaged their physical health, endured appalling living conditions, to make the dream possible. Children as young as seven were sent across the ocean, sent to the altar as sacrifices, to secure futures, not just for themselves, but for their entire families. A last few pennies would be scraped together to buy a new dress for the sojourner. Thus the investment was made.

What was confronted on arrival was, of course, another story. The shock to the system has still not worn off. The education system was familiar, as the British system was in use back Home; but here was the added dimension of racism. The teachers, far from having the best interests of the pupils at heart, started from an assumption of the racial inferiority of Black children, and worked from there. Children who were called names, whose mother tongue was derided, who were tormented not only despite, but often *at the instigation of* white teachers, felt they had no recourse. They often got no support from parents who had made such sacrifices to bring them here, and who could not comprehend that a teacher would do something detrimental to a child. When a teacher approached a parent about putting her child into an ESN school, for example, the mother would respond with total trust, believing that the teacher was actually acting in her child's best interests.

Many Black women and men in their twenties and thirties today write off the older generation, dismissing them as 'too passive', too conformist, saying that they didn't do enough to challenge white racism from the time they arrived here. While it is easy to see why a whole generation, subjected to brutal racism at a very young age by the schools and the police, feel a deep resentment towards their parents' generation who often did not support them, this is too simplistic a view.

Older Black women will say how much worse things have gotten, how 'nice' white people were to them in the 1950s (and 1940s and 1930s). But sometimes the same older Black women, sometimes others, will contradict this, telling stories of white landladies who would not allow them use of the bath. Of employers who remarked, 'We can't give *all* of the jobs to you people.' Of Black bodies found floating in Camden Lock. The Westindian community was under threat in the 1950s in exactly the same way that the Asian community is under threat now. In London, Black women, men and children were attacked in the streets by white gangs, and Black homes were firebombed.

Black people in smaller, more isolated communities are still subject to the same immediate threat of physical violence. One Black woman in Preston, Lancashire, a couple of years ago successfully proved a case of racial discrimination against an employer. The newspaper which published the story printed her name and address in the piece, and she was subsequently attacked in her home by a white supremacist.

The immediate physical threats still exist, as do the more subtle, insidious forms of institutionalized racism. But, while we as Black people living in this white country are every day becoming more aware of the intricacies of the racism labyrinth, racism, too, is changing. It is becoming ever more subtle in its variations. Our priorities are also shifting. In the 1950s it was very simple – get a job and a roof over your head, put food in your children's mouths. Many Black parents were prepared to accept second best for the sake of their children's futures. The next generation is not prepared to settle for that. They demand their rightful place at the table. Still, we must not forget that, were it not for our mothers' sacrifices, we would not be in the room.

The racism they encountered here caused many Black people, who up to then had been very white-identified, to become radicalized. They could not pretend that the injustices they had suffered in Black countries were due to lack of education or lack of money. Even when they arrived as skilled workers or educated professionals, they were denied any but the lowliest jobs. Even when they had money in their hands, they could not find decent housing. The pattern at last became clear, here in the belly of the beast.

It's hard to believe whole races of people could be so naive. So trusting. So brainwashed. But that is the function of the British education system and media – not to inform, but to brainwash.

Growing up in the 1960s in New York was, for me, growing up under the British Invasion. Our airwaves were dominated by London and Liverpool bands' imitations of Blackamerican music and our TV screens were constantly splashed with big red buses, Swinging London's miniskirts and adverts for Yardley cosmetics and London Fog raincoats. I loved the Beatles and the Stones, which was lucky as I literally could not turn on the radio without hearing 'Penny Lane' or 'Satisfaction'. I don't think Afro-Caribbean people in Britain today, who remember looking to Britain as the mother country, have any conception of how strongly the British Invasion influenced a generation of Black and white American youth.

Meanwhile, the Imperial chickens had come home to roost. The children of the Empire, having tasted the crumbs from Britain's table and found them bitter, were beginning to look back over their shoulders, to such US leaders as Angela Davis and Malcolm X, to the Black Power movement, as a source of pride and strength.

I am really glad I have the educational background I have. My knowledge of slavery and all the social behaviours it spawned has given me insight into the types of compromises Black people have had to make, the survival patterns we developed, and so helped me to recognize the response to those survival patterns so evident in racist stereotypes. So, for example, the labelling of Black people as slow, ignorant, lazy, shiftless (read 'passive'), is merely a derogatory labelling of behaviour which Black women and men developed as forms of resistance to slavery.

The fact that this information has been deliberately and systematically kept from us has meant that we have not had at our disposal the tools for adequate analysis. Therefore, instead of understanding the roots of our oppression, we felt guilty, internalized that guilt, and blamed ourselves and others for our predicament. The fact that Black parents traditionally admonish their children that they have to do better at school than white children is, on one level, a statement of fact. But, on another level, it is the continuance of internalization of racism – for you to go ahead, you have to do well according to the standards as they are laid down, not challenge and change the system at its roots. This internalization of guilt, of believing that we are the root cause of our failure or success within this system, is perpetuated from one generation to the next. Its causes go back to the days of slavery and colonization, where white people created a 'buffer' class, sometimes made up of Asians, other times of mixed-race people, who were put above Black people, given more privileges and status. The white people set the standards, which *could not* be challenged. A Black person who had two Black parents could not become mixed-race or Asian. The 'buffer' class, brainwashed into believing they were superior, looked down on the Black people. This was done deliberately, so that neither group would turn on their true oppressors, the whites.

Just as many Black people continue to measure themselves against white standards, rather than challenge them, so many of us have internalized these divisions. Deep-seated rivalries and dissensions exist between African and Afro-Caribbean women, women of African descent and Asian descent, lesbian Black women and heterosexual Black women, mixed-race and 'totally Black' women, etc, etc. These differences, while important, should not be the basis for deep divisions amongst us.

We are always trying to prove we're 'Blacker than' the next person, because we're so insecure about not being 'Black enough'. In this, we have bought into the white stereotyped definition of Blackness as being a very narrow range of physical, behavioural and cultural traits.

We are harshly critical of Black women who choose divergent paths, who choose to interact more with white people, from whom they get most of their support (eg partners of their own white mothers), who choose or don't choose to work with

Asians, to call themselves African, to call themselves feminist, to perm their hair, to wear African dress, to wear jeans. This harsh criticism, this intolerance, turns Black women away, perhaps young Black women who are questioning the society they see around them, or older Black women who are trying to change after a lifetime of conforming to or 'fitting in' with the white model. After one visit to our groups or our centres, they decide they will never fit in, they undervalue their own experience, and they run, not walk, back to their familiar patterns of behaviour and support. Meanwhile, we, in our cosy 'sisterly' nooks, congratulate ourselves on how right-on and aware we are. Is this unity?

Just as white people 'forgot' about us or became oblivious to the fact that we existed during colonization, we are starting to forget about each other. We forget how much courage and strength of will it took for our Black foremothers to come here and set up home in what was the equivalent of an alien world. We forget what it's like to be isolated, what it's like to discover what feminism means, what it's like to realize what racism means for the very first time. We undermine each other's survival mechanisms, rather than respecting the fact that these mechanisms have worked for a lifetime and have, in fact, sometimes kept Black women *alive*.

I have said that I feel very fortunate to have access to the knowledge I have, and to be able to make the connections I make. By the same token, Black British women have access to a completely different set of facts. They know much more than I do about the days of the Raj, about the British dealings with the Ashante, about Cecil Rhodes's actions. Though they may have been shocked by 'Roots', I have been equally shocked by things I have learned.

While it cannot be denied that the Black power movement was of major benefit to Black people in Britain, just as it had impact in the US and in every part of the world where Black people were living, this is not the 1960s. This is the late 1980s. Since I arrived in Britain in 1982, I have met many Black people who thought they could tell me all about America. When they were not insisting I must be Westindian, they were telling me the US was different, 'because we don't have segregation over here'. Had they not heard of the 'colour bar', of signs which read: *'No Blacks, No Irish, No Dogs'*? Did they think that in New York City, Chicago or Boston we had to bow and scrape to whites? Did they not know that, in London, Bristol and Leeds, Black people were confined to ghettos? A recent issue of *Chic* contained an article entitled 'Mr King, Are You Still Dreaming?', which combined a very simplistic analysis of the nature of modern racism in the United States with a total lack of any attempt to link up and dialogue with Black Americans, let alone draw any parallels between the way racism is experienced in Britain and in the US.

I was told emphatically by Black women here that, in the States, women had 'thrown away their wigs!' – forgetting that the US is the home of the perm. By the same token, when I arrived, I expected Brixton to be a burnt-out battle zone, similar to the South Bronx – those were the images we had seen on the news. I thought Black people would live in Black-only neighbourhoods and attend Black schools, similarly to back home. Those of us who are not aware of the similarities are just as ignorant as those of us who cannot see the distinctions. And she who does not learn from others' experience will be condemned to repeat it.

My learning process continues to be an exciting one, and I am eager for cross-cultural exchange among Black women to continue and expand. We are reclaiming scraps for our history, and we must continue to share information we have about our common experience. By the same token, we must always remember that the images we see of ourselves and each other are almost never created by us. We must not take on board these images; we must create and imprint our own. In the process of doing so, we must also remember that no one of us speaks for all Black women. We can only start where we are. No one of us has the right to devalue or dismiss another Black woman or ourselves. As Yvette Cort says in her 'Oral History', we are in danger of stereotyping ourselves. We confuse unity with sameness, diversity with dissent. This is a dangerous mistake. Our differences are our stength.

The process continues. *Sojourn* is a record of some of the many-sided experiences of some Black women in Britain.

Love and Power
Zhana
December 1987

Setting Out

*

To begin, we examine that which birthed us: she who brought us into being, who gave us our earliest memories, our values, ideas, self-concepts – our selves.

*

ZHANA

Beginnings

*

Mother, Black goddess, you laughed and swung your arm in a wide arc, sprinkling stars across the sky. Then you spread your legs and birthed a child, Earth, with its afterbirth, Moon.

Great Mother, sometimes called Great Whore, we loved you once and danced hand in hand with you. When you made love, lava erupted from your volcano breasts, and when you gave birth, waterfalls poured forth from your depths.

The dark, cool earth was your skin on which we rolled, and danced the sacred dance, before you were defiled by the foot of man. We loved you then and we worshipped you, your bears, your bees, your daughters had more daughters in your likeness.

Then the white man came and stole your children, raped the depths of your child, Earth. Defiled your daughters and taught us to be ashamed of the sacred dance. Now we no longer sing to your glory, but we still hold the words of your songs deep within our hearts.

IIOLA ASHUNDIE

Mother of Mine

I remember you when you looked after me when I was ill. You nursed me until I was well again, my dear mother. I ran and played under Grandmother's house making my mud pies and I truly eat them. It tasted like it had been mixed with salt from the sea, then I was ill again. This time I had worms. I screamed as I sat upon the pot; they wiggled and jiggled, as you helped withdraw them from my body. Yes, it was you, my mother.

I watched you when you baked the cassava bread and fried the fish upon the open stove in the yard. You giggled and played with me and your other children, yes, my two brothers and my sister. When it was time to sleep you kneeled beside me making sure that I said my prayers. Yes, I remember, it was 'Gentle Jesus meek and mild', but my tongue told me it was 'Seventy Jesus make a mile'. You slapped me for talking utter nonsense.

Then one day you told me I was going to England. Where it was I did not know, I only knew that the big silver aeroplane took you there high in the sky. I used to shout to it, yelling out to bring me lots of things, little that I knew that it couldn't hear me. You came out into the hot sun, it's radiance brightened your smile as you looked at me. Happy go lucky, I ran about the yard with my sisters and brothers, chasing the fowls up and down, until I stepped on one of the baby chicks, squeezing out its inside. It went all over my foot. I was frightened, I ran under the house to hide myself from you. You were totally vexed. All the shouting that you did couldn't get me out. There I stayed until evening, when you called me for my food. Thinking that you had forgotten about the baby chick, yes, mother, I got a beating that very evening.

On Sundays when you plaited my hair, we popped the peas from their pods. I listened to you and Grandmother laughing. There you sat and put your paper curls in your shiny black hair. Yes, mother, I was there. Again you told me I was going to England and that the snow was going to bite me. I cried because I didn't want the snow to bite me, believing that it was some sort of animal. You said that there was lots of fog too. I hid myself beneath Grandmother's bed, believing that a multitude of frogs was going to get me. I ran along the alley jumping fence, oh so high and mighty, for I was only as small as a flea. Again I had an injury. Yes, mother, I jumped upon a nail so large and rusty. I hopped and cried while you put purple violet upon my feet. I thought I was going to die. For days I could not walk, as the pain went through my thigh.

The hot sun shone down as I ran down the bay. There I stayed catching crabs all day, until they bit my finger so. I hurried home dry as can be, where you told me that I looked like I have just come from salt pan alley. 'Go and get yourself clean up,' you shouted. Indeed, I gleamed as a mirror for I had used all the vaseline.

You told me to go down my Aunt Vicky. I hopscotched all the way. There I was bitten by her dog, Bully.

The star shone from above, yes it was the middle of the night. I was sick again, this time I had diarrhoea. Someone had given me beer. I sat upon the pot, filling it completely, as I emptied the contents of my stomach in another before me. Yes, I remember, I was sick as can be. Then something flickered in the breadfruit tree. It crashed upon the tin roof. I ran as fast as could be and you comforted me. Yes, mother, for I was frightened of Jumbie.

You dressed me in my pretty dress and we went to church. I began to climb the steps. The rude boys began to look up at me from beneath. Little did I realize that I had forgotten to put on my panties. Fancy that, mother, I had forgotten to put on my panties.

I looked at you while you scaled the fish. I ran and scaled the mango tree, even bruising my knee.

The yard was empty. You were not there. Only the fire

flickered there, and little brother began to play there. He said he was making pull-pull-sweetie and how I loved pull-pull-sweetie. It looked so real. He flicked it at me, almost blinding me. My bottom was bare. He had got me there. The scar is still there.

Then again you told me I was going to England and that it was cold as ice. I didn't want to be frozen like ice, like the ice that came upon the donkey cart. Thinking I was smart, I used to pull the donkey's tail. The man said he was going to send me to jail for pulling the donkey's tail.

Something stunk in the air, as the flies were everywhere. I climbed the kitchen top. There I saw Mr Thomas giving the shark the chop.

Once again, mother, you told me I was going to England. How I was going to Daddy. It's funny but I didn't remember him leaving. He weren't there in the evening.

The car drew up. I got inside. I saw the houses going by. You placed me with a guide, who always peeled my hide. You kissed me goodbye and told me not to cry, with my handbag by my side. Oh, mother dear, you were not there as the ship drew in at the pier. I looked up to find my daddy. There were thousands of daddies everywhere. Yes, mother, you were not there. Only sorrow there was to bear.

For many years I tried to get over there, to hear your laughter from your long gone daughter. I grew to be a teenager with children later. Again my thoughts wandered over many waters. The emptiness grew deeper as life grew dimmer, never hearing your laughter. My inner energies began to take hold of me to find you again, my dear mother, to catch that plane to that far-off land.

I walked down the stairs with my ticket in one hand. Someone looked at me. I didn't recognize him, my dear long lost brother.

It was dark as the stars lighted my heart. I stood upon the sidewalk. This old woman stood there. Then I was told it was you, my mother. I looked with wonder, seeing you for the first time. Should I cry, as I hugged you? Yes, mother, I had returned. It seems like a century to fill this heart that is empty. Yes, it's my mother and me, your long lost daughter.

*

ISHA McKENZIE-MAVINGA

Daughters

*

When you were deep inside me.
seed in egg.
Foetus in womb.
conceived and unborn,
in there still.

I pushed you out into the world.
cord unlinked.
waters gone.
breast in mouth.
out there still.

When I left you at the school gates.
knee high.
doll in hand.
Tears in your eyes.
inside me still.

You grew into women.
Body reformed.
meeting others.
being yourselves.
Beside me still.

When you left home.
branching out.
being grown.
tears in my eyes.
Still.

*

ISHA McKENZIE-MAVINGA

Grassroots Mother Daughter

*

Sula's friend was not at school. She had gone home early the previous day, in a mess, with her period, her vagina leaking. It had happened all over one of the school chairs and Sula had helped her to wash her bloodstained socks before she left for home. What shame and embarrassment she had shared with her friend. It was not Sula herself who this time felt the uncomfortable bulge between her legs and glanced behind to see if she had left her stains on the wooden chair. She felt relief at being able to disconnect herself for a while from being a woman. It was now confirmed that she was not the boy she had wished she could be in the early part of her life. It was better for her to forget she had longed for a penis and was almost convinced she had one, when she discovered how easy it was to sit facing the back of the lavatory and pee like a man.

On discovering her womanness, she remembered well the experience of proudness and pain associated with her growing breasts. The inhibiting glances of her peers, the lumps of flesh on her chest bouncing unsupported, until her sister bought her first bra. The mystery of her own menstruation lifted when it was her turn at last to 'come on'. She no longer needed to search for the pink spot of initiation, turning her into a woman. Feelings of isolation and punishment prevailed when her body was changing and her moods were turning blue and grey like the weather on a cloudy day. It was a time when she was unaware of mourning her old body frame and fearing its transformation into a new shape. Her internal metamorphosis linked mysteriously to a new external sexual appearance of her body structure and at the same time was kindred to feelings of shame about being locked inside her brown body.

The appearance of her brown skin created a stir in other people, that she was unclear about. What was clear to her was the feeling of anxiously answering to the term 'half-caste'. She was owning her identity in terms of her mother and father and how the world perceived them judgingly because one was Black and one was white. She was not being accepted in her own right and felt shame at owning her whiteness, or was it her Blackness? The women looking after her in the children's home had not told her who she was.

Memories of being a Black child in care and her transition from childhood to womanhood, flushed and faded in Sula Morina's mind as she made her final efforts to expel the child from inside her body, out into the world. A distant place from the mother and baby home she was now in. The matron in the children's home had seen to it that she would settle up for the wrong she had done by becoming pregnant at sixteen. She was to pay penance by going away where the nuns would see to it that no men would be allowed into the house and only women would preside over the birth. The desired result being that her baby would be put up for adoption. Sold to someone more capable of looking after it. Adoption was the cure for unmarried mothers, because being pregnant at sixteen most certainly meant you would be an unfit mother. Sula, however, had never felt fitter than when the birth of her baby was imminent.

The final phase of the birth engulfed Sula's body like a giant orgasm, complemented by the deep inhalations of gas and air she was encouraged to inhale. As she bore down, deep into the lower parts of her body, the purpose of her journey into motherhood became clearer. Moments later, overwhelmed by the joy of her unique and unforgettable experience, she lay watching the dawn break. The world seemed far away and her inner world unashamedly exposed. She relived moments of revealing secret parts of her body that performed powerfully, controlling her most recent event of childbirth. Her womanhood gaped with a vulnerable urge to be looked after by someone else: the nurse who gently cleaned her up. She wondered at the tiny infant she had just brought into life. Her body felt light as though a great burden had been lifted from it. And she examined the deflated flabby remains of her pregnant belly. Moments before, her baby girl had been inside her and now they seemed far apart. Anea, she had already prepared a name which would signify they were no longer one, but two separate human beings. Her child was already aware of separate needs, comforting herself with a thumb in her mouth. Perhaps in anticipation of the difficult times that lay ahead of them both. Sula was unsure what lay ahead and waited for permission to touch her baby, wondering at what stage Anea would become her own. She desperately wanted to help her baby belong, something she had not experienced herself. Although she had not planned to have a baby so soon, her ambition was to be married and have a happy family to replace the one she had grown up without.

The impact of her new family tie and maternal responsibilities became a reality to Sula when she experienced hearing her baby cry through the night. The nursery seemed far away, beyond her capability of reaching, without risking interference with the nuns' system of running the home. Her first night passed restlessly and she felt compelled, by her fear of authority, to wait till morning to feed her child. At daybreak her baby refused to feed, exhausted from her night's attempts to gain attention and pacified with distilled water and powdered milk.

The nurse pulled Sula's swollen breasts toward the infant's tightly closed mouth and the pain reminded her that she accepted it was her fault the baby would not feed. It was all part of her punishment for getting into trouble so young, when she had not really learnt how to do a mother's job. After a while she became aware that the restrictions they placed on her were unreal in relation to Anea's needs. She knew this did not feel right for her baby even though she could not recall a memory of feeling close to her own mother's breast. The anger she held inside her because her mother was not around to pass on the secrets of childcare prevented her from doing this. Time passed in this way and Sula struggled to become acquainted with her baby as she thought a mother should. The path to motherhood led her into a strange and hostile environment. She was now surrounded with the convictions of the other young women who were also in the mother and baby home. An unequal smear blurred the shared experience they all had of the potential motherhood of illegitimate babies. Sula felt smugness at the idea that her own situation was probably not half as bad as Laura's because Laura was only fourteen and at that age she should not have even been having sex. Then there was Denise who had got fucked at a party and didn't even know who the father was because she was drunk at the time. Sula thought she should have behaved much better at her age – she was twenty-one. Although Sula's own situation seemed somewhat detached from the others, what united them was the unanimous feeling of being punished for what they had done.

All of the young women had been threatened by their parents that if they wanted to keep their babies they were not to return home. To Sula this seemed the most threatening situation she had ever heard. They were coming from the fantasy family homes she had dreamt about, so their loss might be greater than any she could ever have imagined. In her thoughts she pushed herself into second place, feeling smug that at least she did not face the decision of choosing her baby or her family home. She had no parents to present with the object of her teenage pregnancy. She had been staying at her sister's home and intended to return there. Sula watched silently as they tortured themselves with the pending loss of leaving their babies behind. She had not thought much about her own situation and how she also was there because the advice she was given by Evelina, the matron in the children's home where she used to live, was that she should 'have her baby adopted and start a new life'. She was there like the others, incensed by the experience of leaving her own mother and growing up without her in care.

After four weeks of being a mother, thoughts of leaving her baby were far in the back of her mind. She was beginning to feel confident that her work as a mother was improving and that she was developing an understanding of her child that no other person was a part of. They had begun to belong to each other, outside each other now, face to face, in the world. Her need for Anea was as strong as Anea's need for her. In her mind it was no longer an effort to try and do things for her child in the way she would have wanted them done for herself. There seemed to be a natural acquaintance between them, with her response to Anea's needs, feeding, nappy changing, being held close and loved, and Anea responding with her smiles.

It was on a long spring afternoon that Sula discovered she had time to explore her surroundings while Anea slept. While on her journey through the big house, she encountered a situation she had been previously unaware of. Entering a large room on the ground floor, she found herself in the nursery. Hesitating for a while, she allowed her eyes to focus into each cot that stood lining the nursery walls. Each one was the same distance apart as though they had been precisely measured in order to secure their independence. Each one contained a child, with brown skin and curly black hair. Like her own. It was as though she had returned to her own familiar surroundings as a child. She fled, saddened, as though she were being chased by the reality of her childhood. The rumours she had heard about Black babies who were left behind because only the white babies were wanted seemed true. She was enraged by Evelina's conspiracy to lure her into repeating her own experience with her child. She decided then that she was going to take her baby away with her and make a home of her own.

Home then was a room at the top of her married sister's house. It seemed the most sensible place to be. The place where she first saw what it was like to be married and living as a family with parents and children at home. This experience still did not fit into her untarnished fantasy of family life and motherhood. She learnt by helping and watching her sister how to do some motherly thing that would help Anea grow up. These motherly things patterned her life for the following twenty years. Unfulfilled within herself, she went on being a mother. Giving, protecting and creating a place where her children could grow. Two daughters and a son. She belonged to them, so they would belong to her and change the previous pattern of her life. She was mothering her children without being able to identify her own experience of being mothered.

During this period her ability to be a perfect woman, wife and mother was constantly challenged by an unknown entity. Men – who consisted of her fantasy father, absent brothers, her husband and a world dominated by men's views. Her sexual identity had been defined in terms of their opinions of her and who she should be in order to fit in with them. Having a child meant she belonged to its father, forever, until parted by death. With this in mind, she was able to maintain her fantasy of the man she wanted him to be. Somewhere in her head she held the information that they were meant for each other. She did not connect his behaviour with that of the other men she had come into contact with in her life. He was almost as young as her when they first met during school days and he innocently harrassed her into having sex with him. It had been different to when men twenty or thirty years older than her had beckoned to her on the street. Black men called her names like red nigger or dirty half-caste when she did not reply to them. She was frightened of their intimidating sexual advances. Her memories of being beaten up by the boys in the home reminded her that she was unsafe if she did not oblige them. This feeling of unsafeness penetrated her married life. Eventually she became aware that sexual intercourse and mothering had become the only rewarded events in her married life and she decided to quit. On her own, outside the marriage with her three children to care for, she discovered the ability to mother herself. She was now thirty-one and wondered at how she had mothered her children.

Bringing up her third child, a son, meant she was once again faced with the reality of being a woman. A woman passing on woman's things from the experience of being a woman, without a man. When Joa began to show signs of his puberty, she feared her disadvantage at not knowing what it felt like to be growing into a man. The thoughts and feelings she had were those she experienced by being a woman. She remembered she had wanted to be like him when she was a child. It was the way she coped with her fear of not having the power that the men around her seemed to own. She realized that she had taken her daughters' growing for granted. Although they were individuals, they were also women like herself, growing up in her womanly image.

Sula had passed the messages of life on to her girls like a secret culture. They were growing up in her image without many words of explanation passing between them. They had learnt to be young women. Their new task was to be independent individuals. She had given them the endowment to utilize their own power of womanhood. Although Sula knew what gifts she had given them, she found it difficult to identify anything in particular she had done to make this happen. She had just been there beside them, growing herself.

Her children were born to her, she became a woman, yet still she was like a sleeping child. Like a flower unable to open at dawn. When she was thirty she allowed herself to separate from her husband, their father. She was realizing her own potential to power. She crossed the threshold of life. Awaking to wonder at how they had come together. She wondered at their survival. The silent way her children had received the messages she passed on to them. While she was unaware of their beauty and things going on in and around them. Sleeping while they grew. She had mothered all three without being able to identify a mother of her own. Someone who may have passed those things on to her.

She had previously blamed her absent mother for not looking after her and depriving her of the motherly feelings she wanted to know. If her mother were to blame, then Sula would be denying what she had learnt of motherhood without her mother being there. Her mother had been only one person, a woman who went through puberty herself. A woman who could not be blamed for having a child, Sula, whom she was unable to care for without the help and support she needed from her family and Sula's dead father. From what Sula had now learnt she realized that it was not only her mother she could rely on to show her how it was done. If there is no truth in an innate, instinctual mothering, then she must have learnt from the women who looked after her in the home.

In the same way that growing up with white people confused her into denying her Blackness, she had been unaware of her distinctiveness as a woman. For a long time wishing to be white, for a long time wanting to be a man. At the time not knowing those things, but remembering them when she remembered her young daughter, Pena, who had covered her brown skin with Sula's talcum powder. Imitating Sula's femininity and wanting to be white. Anea's need to dress like Marilyn Monroe as she had seen her mother do, and straightening and lightening her hair so she could be accepted by men and envied by women. It reminded her of her own painful efforts to hide her Blackness from the world. They had watched and been part of her struggle and now they were sorting it out for themselves. Sula was angry sometimes on seeing her daughters weeping and washing away their childhood as they struggled to become young women, trying to be like mother yet wanting to be themselves. Sula wanting them to be like her yet separate as strong, independent women. This struggle blurred the memories of her own puberty and loss of childhood. She herself was imitating a mother image she had silently internalized, not understanding how this came about.

Unable to find the answers for them, she watched Anea and Pena repeat the same struggle within themselves to be themselves. Consoling herself that their growing was aided by her presence, that she had achieved for them what was missing for herself. To experience the security of having a mother present while they were growing up. Hoping that the seeds of a new family structure have again been sown.

*

NAJMA KAZI

Conflict

*

Great Britain, the land of plenty, its streets paved with gold. I came to Britain in 1963, in Harold Macmillan 'You've never had it so good' time. I wonder if Pakistanis today, unacquainted with Britain, still think of Britain as the land of opportunity. A place to come to earn a living, but a place where they would not dream of settling, a place unsuitable for bringing up families, children.

As a child in Karachi, I did not view our coming to Britain as an uprooting experience. Far from it. The prospect of travelling to Britain filled me with excitement and a sense of adventure, the thrill of being in Europe, of seeing a country that just a few years before my birth had ruled mine. As a child in Karachi I could not but be aware of Britain's legacy. Take my first school in Karachi, a Catholic establishment, St Patrick's. It was at St Patrick's that I first became familiar with English rhymes, names and places. My subsequent schools, though not as prestigious as St Patrick's, nevertheless were set up in the tradition of English schools.

So the prospect of coming to Britain after all I read about it was like a dream come true. It was curious to see it all, to experience it, and to see the riches of Britain. I was eager to have the textbook vision of Britain confirmed by my own eyes. I had a picture-postcard view of Britain, of snow-covered rooftops, fields and hills, particularly at Christmas time.

I was captivated by the city of London and was very disappointed on my arrival in Britain to find that I was not going to be living in London. We lived in a quiet place, Farnborough.

My first Christmas in Britain was a bit of a let-down. There was none of the expected snow. I thought it would magically appear on Christmas morning. But what a disappointment. I had to content myself with songs on TV, 'Dreaming of a white Christmas'. I was eager to see how people here celebrated their big festivals. I found the day dull, apart from the TV programmes. No one was out in the streets, no kids showing off their toys, new clothes. Not at all like Eid.

We were initially a novelty. We were one of a handful of non-white families in Farnborough. Our colourful clothes were admired, in particular the saris my mother wore. But no one thought much of my shalwars, and after the initial period of politeness I used to get teased in the streets about wearing my pyjamas. I was very sensitive to all this teasing, some of it quite unpleasant. And I think this was the beginning of my feelings of insecurity about being Asian* in Britain. As a child I would have preferred to remain invisible. I would have preferred people not to notice that there was anything different about me. I became very self-conscious about myself, my dress, the way I looked, though stubbornly I continued to wear my shalwars. And something else. Though I stubbornly continued to wear my shalwars I did not care to come across any other Pakistani or Indian women in the streets who also wore shalwars. This happened unconsciously over a period of time, and was for me a very conflicting and disturbing discovery about myself. How had this happened, and why did I, as a teenager, begin to feel ashamed of my own people, in particular other women from my community?

Once I left school I discarded my shalwars altogether and did not wear them again until I was well into adulthood. The then image of the shalwar as a dowdy, unsmart garment had lodged firmly in my mind. Unflattering baggy trousers. As a teenager living in Britain, I only wanted to project those areas of my native culture which the natives of my adopted country approved of, found attractive and worthy to hang on to. The sari fitted into this image. Graceful, diaphanous drapery, glamourous and sexy. The sari was certainly the more acceptable 'ethnic' dress.

These were the liberal Sixties. The Race Relations Act had

*The term 'Asian' as used here refers to people from the Indian subcontinent. It is a white-defined term and the subject of another article.

been passed and integration was the buzz word. The Act seemed a reason to be optimistic about the future. If the government was prepared to acknowledge the injustice of racism by passing an act making it illegal in certain areas then surely things could only get better. Also, in my teenage naïvety I had this idea that racism would not affect me because I lived in a predominantly white area. The area I lived in was not a 'ghetto'. Racism was only a problem in 'ghettos' like Southall. I had no positive images of places like Southall or Bradford. I saw them as dangerous and unsafe. I was glad I did not live in such places. Too many of our people living in overcrowded conditions. Couldn't they see they were asking for trouble? I had of course never ventured into such areas. I imagined I was more integrated into British society because I lived in a predominantly white area. I was mixing. I was doing my bit towards integration.

At the same time I decided that Britain was not for me. I did not want to spend the rest of my life here, in this cold land. Britain was not home. I also missed my friends. I remember telling my father that I would return to Karachi as soon as I became economically independent. I did not then, or could not then, imagine or appreciate that living my formative years, or even just living a long time, in Britain would bind me to this place in more ways than one.

Living in a white area did not put a stop to me being at the receiving end of racist taunts and abuse. In fact in my isolation I was more vulnerable not just in terms of being the target but, more importantly, in terms of my ability to deal with racism. I was ill-equipped to deal with racism without always having to justify my presence in Britain. At that time the term 'Paki' had not become the general term of abuse for people from the Indian subcontinent. We Asians were not then assigned this distinctive term of abuse. My first memory of direct racist taunts goes back to my second year of my secondary school, when two boys in my class started referring to me as 'nigger' or 'darkie', whatever came to their fancy.

Awareness and experience of racism brought to the surface feelings of collective responsibility. I – no, not just I but we, I mean the whole of the non-white community in Britain – was accountable, and had to be beyond reproach in our attitudes and behaviour. I remember feeling ashamed on reading in the paper about any unlawful or criminal activity involving 'coloured' people, as we were often referred to then. I felt that we must not give the white host community any grounds for confirming their worst fears about us. Almost as if we had to prove that we were worthy of living here. We had to always be on our best behaviour. The 'host' community could of course behave how they liked. It was after all 'their' country.

Linked with this feeling of collective responsibility was the feeling that we were here on sufferance and our security here depended on carefully controlling our numbers here. I absorbed the ideas of immigration controls as a necessity, for our own long-term good, and of course for the good of race relations. With every press report about people from Pakistan or India trying to enter Britain illegally I felt embarrassed. Here we were in the news again; more of us trying to enter Britain, so making life that much more difficult for those of us already here through legal channels.

From my experience of racism and the contradictions that it has generated in me and also from talking to fellow Asian Britons I know that I was not alone in having harboured the feelings of insecurity that I relate. Racism has damaged me. Racism has damaged us all psychologically, has caused us to internalize it into self-dislike. Racism has given us an abnormal inhuman perspective about ourselves as people. This abnormal perspective resulted in the kind of symptoms I experienced as a teenager, being ashamed of my own people, of wearing my clothes, of talking too loudly in Urdu or Hindi in public places and so on. Acknowledging this psychological damage and writing about it is to take a step towards reversing it. The healing process has begun. Without acknowledging this damage we cannot extend or expect real solidarity with each other here in Britain or with our sisters in the subcontinent. Without acknowledging this damage, any solidarity that we do manage to extend to each other will always be within the constraints imposed by the white world.

Racism has stunted our growth and development on another level. Even when I became politicized and my politicization extended to my active involvement in the Asian/Black movements, Asian Women's groups, there was always this dilemma that because we lived in a racist white-dominated society we should not and could not afford to be openly critical of our own people, the oppressive aspects of our culture, the oppression imposed on us, our patriarchy. The logic behind this self-censorship was, and is, that in exposing our weaknesses we will provide white people with information to use as ammunition against us and to divide and so to control and rule us further. But history shows that our very presence in this country, indeed the world, is ammunition enough to white people. My contention is that in taking this stand we yet again allow white people to dictate to us the terms of our growth, our development, our emancipation as people, as Asian women. In all the Asian groups I have been involved with or come across we talked about our right to organize autonomously. I now feel that all this talk was just lip-service and a sham.

The sad truth is that we have not dared to discuss issues of vital concern to us except within the framework set by white people. To our detriment we have censored ourselves. In one Asian group I was active in some years back, one of the men maintained that Asian women had taken up the cause of feminism at the instigation of white women. As if somehow we were incapable of protesting in our own right and interests, and that women's issues were of no concern to us. Asian men constantly throw at us the accusation that when we protest and take up issues of concern to us as women we are aping white women. Similarly our sisters in the subcontinent when they take up issues of concern to themselves are accused of wanting to ape the West. To protest is unIslamic or unIndian. We must be clear that this accusation only serves to fuel the myth that protest is a monopoly of white people, of white women, that protest and the fighting of oppression are only legitimate when white people, white women engage in it.

In my experience censorship of the not-so-nice aspects of our culture has also occurred in an Asian Women's group. To collude with Asian men and women by remaining silent about the oppressive aspects of our culture is to deny our own traditions of protest both against white colonialism and against oppression within our own culture. It is to acquiesce to white domination and I for one do not wish to collude with this position.

As an adult I have returned to Pakistan for brief visits and for a longer working visit. Both Pakistan and Britain are home in their different ways, yet neither is home. To persist in calling Pakistan home without qualification is to ignore the economic realities that brought us here in the first place, and to ignore the effects of our long sojourn here. I think that for many of us returning to our 'homeland' would be as much an uprooting experience as the initial uprooting from the subcontinent to Britain. Equally, to see Britain as home without qualification is to ignore the realities of racism and of how racism has distorted our outlook.

The Storms that Rend Us

*

The experience of violence at the hands of Black and white men is perhaps less talked about, but certainly no less prevalent in our lives, than is racism. Black women live in constant fear of the physical and psychical brutality which is used to control us, and to which we often lose our lives. Not only are we subject to this violence, we are often party to it.

There is no worse betrayal than that by Black women. By our mothers, sisters and friends, by those in whom we have placed all of our faith, trust and love, by those who are most like us. To men, to whites, to the dominant values of this society. The betrayals we survive leave us with deep wounds, almost ineradicable scars.

ZHANA

Mother/Daughter

My relationship with my mother has always been a difficult and painful one. We have fought and struggled, argued and threatened each other. I have often felt I was the only person in the world to have this problem. Trying to get some support in my problems with my mother was a dead end. Other Black women's reaction tends to be 'but our mothers do so much for us', as if this precluded our criticizing them in any way, let alone admitting that there were serious problems in our relationships. I felt the guilt that women often feel when we are victims: we have no right to complain, it's all our fault.

As a Black woman, the guilt was, for me, multi-layered. I should be glad to have the 'luxury' to be in a position to examine mother/daughter relationships when most Black people were so busy coping with 'real' problems. As a feminist and, later, Blackwomanist. I was proud to have had such a strong, dominant mother figure as a role model. Yet, with this pride came the shame that I should be so unsisterly as to criticize her, let alone complain that she had abused me. The 'sisterhood' line goes something like this: 'We must all stand together to applaud each other's strengths. Any suggestion that these "strengths" are abuses amounts to breaking ranks, colluding with the enemy.' I am still, painfully, unlearning the idea that Black solidarity means unquestioning loyalty.

There is a huge taboo against talking, or even thinking, about our mothers in any but the most clichéd terms. 'She's so strong/ they've done so much for us/made so many sacrifices' are phrases that come up time and again like emotional screens blocking out any rational challenge or dissent.

When I was little, I used to wish my mother was dead. As I grew older, my wish grew into an elaborate fantasy until, in maturity, I came to realize that, even if she were physically dead, she would continue to live in my psyche.

My mother used to disapprove of everything I did, everything I wanted to do. She was totally inhibiting. Being in the same room with her meant being subjected to a series of don'ts – don't laugh so loud, don't sit like that, don't walk that way, and don't say that – above all, don't say that. This strongly undermined my confidence and caused me to lack faith in my own judgement and instincts from an early age. It also caused me to be terrified of other people, believing that I would receive universal disapproval from everyone I met. I believed that my mother disapproved, not of my behaviour, but of my very existence. If she so fundamentally disapproved of my being, how could anyone else feel otherwise?

Our biggest bone of contention was, and is, my weight. When I was a little girl, I was small for my age and very thin. Between the ages of five and seven, I had a serious illness which left me even thinner. My mother was probably worried that people would think she wasn't feeding me properly. She put a lot of pressure on me to eat up and, being a little girl who craved the approval of her parents, I did. By the time I was eight, I was the same size and weight as any other child my age. I kept eating and growing so that, by age ten, I had developed a pot belly of which I was acutely conscious.

The term 'painfully shy' might be a cliché, but in my case it is very descriptive of how I felt at that age. Opening my mouth in public caused me acute psychological discomfort akin to physical pain. I was convinced that everything I did or said was wrong and that I would be told off for being in any way 'different'.

Both my parents were working full-time by the time I was six. We had to get up in the dark and cold so that they could make sure we were dressed and fed by the time they went to work at

7.30. I used to hate it. We had to leave for school by 8.15. It was a fifteen-minute walk, but I always managed to be late.

By the time I was ten, I was into a routine. A bowl of potato crisps dipped in ketchup before school. Either a bit of reading – I was into Kipling – or some TV. After school, another bowl of potato crisps with ketchup, followed by a bowl or two of ice cream and maybe some pretzels, perhaps more potato crisps if I thought their absence would go unnoticed. I hid the bowls under the living-room furniture, sometimes for days at a time.

My favourites were the ice-cream sandwiches – rectangles of vanilla ice cream sandwiched between melt-in-your-mouth chocolate wafers. There were twelve in a box and I could eat six in one sitting – the only thing that stopped me was my parents' disapproval. Ice-cream sandwiches were the best. The rest I could take or leave. But I felt a compulsion to eat, to feel food in my mouth, to taste. The guilt I experienced was crushing, devastating. I honestly believed I was a bad person because I was 'overweight', because I 'couldn't control' my eating. These were the days of Twiggy, of women who didn't have busts, let alone waists. I used to sit in front of the TV for hours watching 'Bewitched', 'The Avengers' and 'I Dream of Jeannie', heroines like Diana Rigg, Barbara Eden and Elizabeth Montgomery parading before my eyes; young, white, slim, beautiful, slender, svelte, stylish, above all, thin. Slim is beautiful is slim.

I wanted to be like those women. I wanted to be able to fit into stylish clothes. I'd put food into my mouth, then will the weight off again. I desperately wanted to be thin. To have no abdomen at all was my ideal. What I really needed was someone to talk to. Instead of talking, I ate. I needed loving arms around me, comforting me, telling me it was okay to be shy, it was okay to be afraid of people, it was okay to be in my body. Instead, the taste and feel of food in my mouth comforted me. But with every mouthful, my guilt increased. I didn't deserve to eat the things I wanted – that was wrong, evil and wicked. I didn't deserve anything. A person who feels she doesn't deserve to eat feels completely unworthy. Some of the feelings engendered then still remain with me today.

My mother would not and could not help me. She didn't believe I was okay because she did not accept herself, and she saw me as an extension of her. My mother is not a fat woman but she has more than a few curves. Instead of being proud of the fullness and roundness of her womanly body, however, she is ashamed of them. A woman's body should take up as little room on the planet as possible, seems to be her attitude, and it should call as little attention to itself as possible. Ever since I can remember, she has been on a diet, but she has never lost any weight.

At this time of my life, starting when I was ten and lasting throughout my teens, my mother was constantly at me to eat less, go on a diet, lose weight, 'control' my eating. 'Calories, Cynthia, calories,' was a phrase frequently tripping off her lips. 'Do you think you should be eating that?' was another. This type of interaction was torture for me, making me feel worse and doing nothing to improve my relationships with food and with my body. And causing me to hate and resent my mother more and more.

My mother left for work at 7.30 each morning and arrived home at 6.00 each evening. When I was younger, I resented the fact that she was not home waiting for me like the other kids' mothers when I returned from school. But by the time I was ten, the resentment was giving way to relief when she left in the morning and dread when she returned at night. I can never remember my mother reading to me when I was school-aged, resting her hand on my head (for fear of mussing up my hair?) or putting her arm around me. I can remember her nagging, criticizing and finding fault with me at every opportunity.

I must have been about twelve when my mother told me I would never have any friends because I was fat, no boy would ever ask me out and, if I went to a party, no one would want to dance with me. I believed her then. Part of me probably still does. (When I was twenty-four, she told me that my friends liked me because 'fat people are supposed to be jolly'. When I left college, she changed her line – now I couldn't get a good job unless I 'made a good appearance', ie lost weight.)

This depressed, angered and pained me so much. I felt my

body was wrong and I was wrong in it. I believed my mother hated me and wanted to destroy me, and I equated her desire for me to lose weight with a wish that I would disappear altogether.

Writing about these problems in my relationship with my mother, most of which I have never written or spoken about before, has freed up a lot of my emotions. It has lessened the anger I feel against my mother while increasing the anger I have against this society, the society which puts Black women in the position of having to make choices which no human being should have to make. Have a career or be a mother, provide for your children materially or emotionally; buy a new hat or pair of shoes or give a hug or a word of encouragement. Be tough, be strong, deny your emotions. The cult of the 'strong Black woman' is lethal. She is never allowed to be weak, be vulnerable. She cannot be the things this society says every woman should be – soft, gentle, caring. She doesn't care for herself, so how can she care for others? Nor can she be what is termed a 'proper mother', all loving, all giving, always there when you need her. In fact, she can't ever be there when she is needed. If the child is sick, she has to go to a neighbour – Mother is working. If the child falls and skins a knee, physically or emotionally, if the child feels unsure or unsteady, she just has to bite her lip and get on with it, for she, too, will be expected to be a 'strong Black woman', and the training begins in infancy.

No woman should have to make these choices. No human being can or should be all things to all people, always on call, always ready with a kind word or a helping hand. Feminism has taught us to distrust and discard traditional sex roles. Yet, it has also taught us how destructive is the image of the 'macho' father, the provider who never has to show his feelings, never shares his emotions, is even afraid of feeling. If it is destructive for men to behave this way in the context of family and relationships, how much more so for women? A little girl (or boy) learns most of her behaviour patterns in relationships from her first relationship, that with her mother. These patterns may stay with her for life.

Now, whenever I see a Black woman, particularly an older one, I see my mother in her, and my immediate expectation is one of disapproval and rejection. To be accepted and acknowledged by a Black woman is a pleasant surprise for me, and to be respected, loved or cared for by Black women is something I almost can't accept. Although wonderful when it happens, it frightens me. I crave it yet fear it. I still sometimes expect Black women who are affectionate towards me to turn on me. I carry within me a vast, gaping wound, one which hurts, some days more than others. When I pass a Black woman at the bus stop and I see her looking me up and down, staring at my belly with (what I perceive as) disapproval; when I walk past a group of Black girls and I hear them whispering and giggling; I feel the whole cycle starting again.

The relationship with the mother is a child's primary relationship and, some say, forms the basis of all other relationships. If my own mother, of whom I was a replica, did not love me, I believed no one would. If I was not safe in her arms, I was safe nowhere.

My mother sees my two sisters and myself as extensions of her body and her personality. She tried to repress me so much because she was so repressed herself, and because she was afraid. Mother is forever telling me, 'people' won't like this or that that I say or do. She has conjured up in her mind a whole universe populated by 'people' who disapprove of her every word, look, thought or action, so that she must be constantly vigilant to remain within the bounds of what is conventional, what is considered acceptable or 'normal'. This fear of appearing out of line extends to such relatively routine behaviours as wearing contact lenses and having pierced ears. My mother lied to me to prevent me from wearing contact lenses because they were something she did not understand, something new and different and therefore not to be trusted. She kicked up a fuss when I pierced my ears at age thirteen and was convinced for weeks afterwards that if I did not (painfully) douse my ears every night with alcohol, I would develop an infection. Several years after that, she had her own ears pierced – I had now proved that it was 'safe'. When I was twenty-four, she objected to me keeping a whisky bottle in my room because it 'wasn't nice' for a 'young lady' to do so.

This obsession with propriety has been analysed as a holdover from slavery when no Black woman was permitted to think of herself as a 'lady'. That which was unattainable became most treasured.

Slave women were often not even permitted to think of themselves as mothers. In Africa, Black women's primary role had been to be fertile, to produce children. They were proud of this role, which gave them status in society. As slaves in the Caribbean and the US, this role was perverted by white slavemasters who used Black women as breeders. They tried to break up the family unit by selling Black women's children away from them, and used this humiliation as a form of behaviour control to keep Black women in line. Black mothers saw their mother role debased.

In modern times, Black women saw our role as strong Black women in the community used once again as a stick to beat us with. The Moynihan Report claims that the 'Black Matriarchy' lies at the root of the ills which afflict the Black community. The Moynihan Report was widely accepted by Black men in the 1960s and 1970s who used it as an excuse to tell Black women we must walk ten paces behind them, in order to avoid interfering with their progress and advancement.

A Black mother, of course, has the worst of all worlds. As a mother, she is never right and she has a host of doctors, psychologists and other 'experts', usually white and male, ready to tell her why she isn't right.

She may believe her mother made mistakes and she may wish to avoid repeating them, which leaves her feeling she is operating in a void, without the benefit of experience to draw from. If she does what society says is proper behaviour for a mother – staying home and looking after her children – she is doing what few Black women have done before and she may feel 'un-Black'. If she goes out to work, to acquire the material comforts she wants and is told by this consumer society she and her children should have, she is being 'unfeminine' (read 'Black Matriarch'). If, like so many women from the Caribbean in the 1950s, and thousands of Black women before them, she travels to a new land in order to secure the best possible future for herself and her family, her children resent her for not being there the way a mother is supposed to be, or for uprooting them from their home and planting them in a new and strange environment.

My mother wanted to avoid at all costs being labelled a 'bad mother'. She saw society's disapproval of me spilling over into disapproval of her. If my mother's worst fears came true and I had no friends, no social life, I couldn't make a good marriage, I had no social standing or prestige in the community or even material security, this would affect her standing as a mother. She couldn't very well brag to her friends, 'My daughter's going down to the dole office today. No one will hire her 'cause she's too fat. If I'd raised her to be slimmer, she could have had a husband to support her.' In her eyes, she would be a failure as a mother.

I used to resent her for her failure even to question the status quo, her (what I saw as) blind acceptance that she and all of us must adopt the white-male-dominated value system of those in control in this society. I saw her as not caring whether her children, whom she should have protected, were chewed up and torn apart by that value system. Not giving any support to those who challenged the forces of oppression. Because she was my mother, I saw her as all-powerful. But what chance does one Black woman have against all of society's destructive power?

Because my mother bought what society was selling, she learned to hate herself. As a woman, you cannot win. You have a vagina, ie lack a penis, lack virility, power, style, everything worth having, while meanwhile you bleed, you smell, you drip (of course, men's bodies don't do these things). My mother's shame at these attributes is written all over her, the way she sits and walks, the way she breathes. She is unhappy in her body, as I am not at home in mine. In a female body, she knows she is wrong. With this knowledge comes the fear that she will be punished by society for being wrong. She can be raped, she can be made pregnant and then blamed for her mistake. It used to hurt me so much to see her doing this to *herself*, to see this strong, powerful woman tightening her own bonds.

Then, there is being Black. In Freudian terms, you are associated with shit: we smell (again). We are too loud, too boisterous, we are bestial and unintelligent. White people believe this and can hold us back unless we prove to them that we are 'worthy'. My mother bought all this – she didn't see the other goods on sale – took it home, and tried to mend it, tried to make it right. If you just play by the rules, eventually maybe they'll let you in the game. So many Black people, men and women, confront society's racism with 'just a few more papers and they'll have to accept me'. Just a few more O-levels, a few more degrees, and the gods will smile on me. I'll be acknowledged for my good work. Never mind the fact that Black people have made multitudinous contributions which have gone unrecognized or been conveniently 'forgotten'. If I just do one more thing right, then they'll have to give me my prize.

The prize my mother was after was acceptance, but she never managed to analyze the root cause of her initial rejection. Like so many Black people of her generation, she believed that all she had to do was to 'prove' to white people how capable she was, and she could overcome their racism. She confused acceptance with power.

I never bought these goods, they weren't good enough for me. I was prepared to go naked rather than to don the cloak of 'good girl' or 'good Nigger'. Not that I was aggressive towards white people, by any means, I simply did not care. The fact that Black people close to me had rejected me so fundamentally made me not care even more. My mother must have sensed this attitude in me from a very early age, and it must have terrified her. What I considered to be mere self-expression, she saw as rebellion. It started with my body rebelling, not fitting into the right clothes, not staying within the bounds of decency of size. If I walked around, this fat girl, not caring, openly if silently rebelling, I would be slaughtered by society. The precious fruit of my mother's womb would be destroyed. My mother could see this clearly as if it were already happening, for in her mind it was happening already every day.

If I survived, that would be almost worse! Then society would be wrong, a whole lot of 'people' would have been forced to accede to one person's (my) demands (to be left alone to follow my own path). A whole heap of generations of Black women would have sacrificed their essence, not talked too loud, not laughed too much, not tried unusual career options, not explored their sexuality – for nothing. Okay, they might already think it had been for nothing, but for me to prove it in flesh and blood was tantamount to rubbing their noses in it. So my mother was furious with me, and terrified for me, from a very early age.

My mother, like many *petit bourgeois* Black people of her generation, had no time for the Black Power movement and the political changes it engendered. Rather than liberating them, they saw these movements as threatening their whole belief systems. To my mother, big Afros were merely scruffy and unkempt, a threat to the old order. Hair was another part of the body which was refusing, at that time, to remain within the bounds of decency and size. Many older Black people now react in the same way to dreadlocks. They fear them, and react with a gut-level disgust against what someone is showing them they could become. Their potential, to expand, to grow in abundance, is almost more than they can handle. Just sit down and shut up, and maybe the lynch mob will pass us by, is their attitude. So imagine their resentment when we make a lot of noise, demand what is rightfully ours, and *get it!* All that fear, all that terror, all that vigilance on behalf of societal norms, was for nothing – or so they think.

If these older Black people could only appreciate the fact that it was because of their efforts, their sacrifices, that we can now demand what is rightfully ours, if only they realized that we are walking along the road that they built, the problem would be halved.

Behind my mother's eyes there churns a deep well of pain and fear, terror and, I am sure, somewhere, anger. Anger that she has been forced to make the choices she has made, that she has never explored her full human potential. Anger at society as well as at herself. But she is too frightened to change. Behind every Black woman's eyes, the same well churns. In some it is deeper than others. In all of us, there is a deep love of what we are, of our true human wholeness and beauty and blessedness, and a love of each other. Some of us allow it to surface, while in others it lies deep below the waters of negativity. The fearful ones are terrified to allow the love of themselves which they recognize in each other to come to the surface, because they aren't used to it. So they bury it in themselves and try to drown it in others in more condemnation, more criticism, more negativity. When these Black women's eyes meet, they turn from each other in fear. When these eyes meet, there shines the truth.

As I grew older, I came to realize that I was not the only one who had these feelings. I watched friends and acquaintances of mine whose mothers were violent towards them, physically and emotionally, and I wondered, 'Is this normal? Is this the way it is meant to be between us?' I wondered where the motherly affection was I saw in the movies, where the cool hand on the forehead was, the soft voice asking, 'Have you had a hard day?' The arm comforting around the shoulder. Was it all a myth?

I experienced the bitchiness that little girls and young women and mature adults practise, the back-stabbing, the gossip. And I asked myself, time and time again, the same questions: are we all like this?

Discussions of the issues in this book between myself and other Black women revealed that we were often going along to meetings with Black women when, in fact, we were literally not on speaking terms with our mothers, perhaps not having seen them or spoken with them for years. In the name and cause of sisterhood, we were meeting about issues which we defined as being relevant to the Black community while being, ourselves, alienated from the very foundation of the Black community – the family, and our own families. Often we had been rejected by them, and equally often we had rejected them. We frequently dismissed our mothers and sisters and other Black women like them because they did not measure up to some standard of politicization as we defined it.

In this context, it becomes essential that we define 'sisterhood' as it means to us. If our sisters are people we don't communicate with or 'can't see eye to eye with', if our mothers and daughters are people we abuse, ignore and reject, then it becomes apparent that when we address each other as 'sister' we are insulting, verbally abusing or at the very least distancing ourselves from each other.

In light of this, it is essential that we go back to basics, strip down our terms and start again to pinpoint just where we are, so that we may chart our course and begin again.

Because we have, as yet, failed to do this, when Black women get together in our spaces, we're still digging at each other, clawing at each other. Instead of the preoccupation with how to be most attractive to men that ruled us in our teens, we're vying for the position of 'most right-on'. We think we have the right to scorn another sister who talks differently or dresses differently, who doesn't use the uniform of language which we find acceptable. If someone is wearing a miniskirt or tight jeans – aha! Something to seize upon, a chance to condemn a sister. At last – what a relief, I thought we'd have to spend the whole day (or meeting or conference) being tolerant with each other. It's such an effort to get on, even though we feel warmth and love for each other, it's so hard to remain on friendly, generous terms. And it's so easy, so bloody easy, to find fault, to find reasons why we can't see eye to eye, can't work together, never, not in a million years.

I believe this goes back to our family relationships, our mother/daughter and sisterly struggles, in which we didn't trust people who looked just like us, ate the same food, slept under the same roof. We were constantly being undermined and condemned by those closest to us, we couldn't trust them, and eventually we learned to play the same game. We got to be better at it than the last generation, we won the prize for being able to find the most fault, and we have now enshrined the game into a cult, all in the name of being politically aware. So, on one team, you have those who insist on the 'political' meaning of the word Black, glowering across at the Africans-only team. Or you have the 'race first – we must stand by our men' group opposite the 'Black feminism/sisterhood is powerful' lot. I begin to wonder, who are we fighting, our oppressors or each other? Actually, I don't wonder at all, I can see we're spending all our time and energy in fighting amongst ourselves.

I include myself in this criticism. I'm as likely as the next person to take up my position and stand unbendingly upon it. All I am suggesting is that, as none of us is perfect, we must continue to try to learn from each other!

Resentment comes from both sides of the generation gap. Too many Black women in their teens and twenties and thirties have no time for older Black women, see them as stick-in-the-muds or, that damning indictment, not radical enough, not aware. Rather than take the time to educate other Black women, not all of whom are older, but who may espouse oppressive attitudes of internalized racism or sexism, we turn our backs on them, we don't want to know. None of us is free until all of us are free, and we're getting nowhere by patting ourselves on the back as to how 'aware' we are, with a superior air. There is a prevalent attitude among many Black women in London today that we have all the answers, that we are the 'first' whatever, that no one can tell us anything. Until we are willing to learn from other Black women, from other generations, other countries, other backgrounds and experiences, we are going nowhere.

The resentment and distrust which is still rife amongst us is a holdover from the days when Mother was all-powerful and we could, in her eyes, do nothing right because *she* could do nothing right. When we meet a Black woman who expresses an opinion or exhibits a mode of behaviour or dress that we associate with internalized oppression, we overreact because we see our mothers in her again, telling us we are wrong, with the full weight of society's might behind her. We don't want to listen to her, we don't want to give her space to be herself, because what she is threatens us. We feel it undermines the gains we have made so far in challenging oppression. This behaviour towards other Black women, then, leads to us being labelled 'extreme' – further intolerance, further misunderstanding. And the cycle continues. Out of our siege mentality, we are even apt to label any political belief which does not agree with our uniform-think as coming from a place of internalized oppression. We are too afraid to allow another sister to be different, to be unique. We are too afraid that she is all-powerful and that her disapproval can destroy us.

As Black people in Britain, we are facing crucial, life-threatening problems at this time. Our families are being broken up by the immigration laws, our young people are still being destroyed in the school system. Black men and women are being battered and killed by the police. In these times, surely, we must come together, with full regard and respect for our differences, to work on our common aims. Until we are honest and open about how we feel about each other, the hatred, the anger, the fear and the love, those feelings will remain buried under the surface, lurking, ever ready to spring out and divide us. We are not being honest when we say 'we are all sisters together', as if those problems either never existed or didn't matter, or don't matter now. The rivalries, the stresses, the self-hate arising from our fundamental relationships have not gone away. We cannot begin to solve these problems if we remain afraid to address them. And until we do begin to address our personal politics, we have no basis on which to discuss the wider issues, because we have no basis on which to define them. We cannot talk about threats to the Black community if we are alienated from the fundamental unit of the community, the family, if we are sitting in a Black women's meeting with our 'sisters' and we are not even on speaking terms with our blood sisters, and we aren't even admitting it. We are not discussing it, even acknowledging it.

Fortunately, this is changing. Recent work by white feminists, notably Adrienne Rich's *Of Woman Born* and Nancy Friday's *My Mother/My Self*, has been very valuable in breaking new ground by exploring, and exposing, the mystique of motherhood. However, in both these works, Black women are notably invisible (surprise, surprise). Audre Lorde's book, *Zami: A New Spelling of My Name*, deals frankly with her growing up and her relationship with her mother and sister. And Black women in Britain are beginning to write about family relationships, about how their mothers sometimes betrayed them by being loyal to fathers and stepfathers who were abusing or raping them. Men have divided us for a long time and we have kept their silences, but now, at last, our lips are opening and the pain and anger is beginning to spill out. And slowly, as the poison drains out, our relationships are starting to heal.

We must be totally honest in discussing the positives that we get from our relationships with our mothers, daughters and sisters. The positives for us, as Black women, often take the form of survival skills. We are grateful to our mothers for teaching us good hygiene and grooming, how to cook and run a home. We often have experiences of seeing our mothers hold down a paying job(s) while also running a home, and being assertive in various situations. I remember, when I was about five, hearing that my mother had gotten into an argument with a man in a supermarket who had insisted that she take meat from the top of the pile. She took the meat she wanted from the bottom of the pile, the fresher meat with the later sell-by date. This was an early lesson in assertion and anti-racism for me.

Black mothers are more likely than white mothers to insist that their children have a good education, and to plan a career for their daughters. Black mothers know that their daughters cannot count on having anyone else to support them, and make a point of teaching us survival and independence from an early age.

Our mothers did a lot for us, and we know it. They loved us, although they may have had a funny way of showing it. They survived, they struggled on, they were role models which gave us the strength and courage to carry on, to try one more time. We know what our mothers have done for us, but it's not enough just to mouth tired old clichés. The time is now for us to discuss and decide what it is about our cultures, our communities, our backgrounds, that we want to keep, along with what we want to discard. Until we honestly admit to the hatreds, the fears, the sufferings that we inflict on each other as Black women, we cannot begin to talk about the positives, the good things, and we are still dismissing our mothers' generations out of hand. If we are not prepared to begin to examine the bad things, we are not even seeing the good.

My mother is now living in Hawaii, campaigning for Dr Martin Luther King's birthday to be made a State holiday. I'm really pleased for her and proud of her.

ISHA McKENZIE-MAVINGA

Death of Yasmin

Daughter of freedom
emerged in
yet separate from
mother's love.

Your lifeless body
lifted,
placed inside
the warm earth.

A mother's task complete,
fufilled,
yet unfilled.
Bits left undone,
unsaid.

Too late now
too late
to become those things
you would become,
done those things
you would have done.

Mother's hopes
when you were small.
Now you are grown
and gone
gone from the conflicts

of human life
gone
gone from the conflicts
gone from human life
gone.

At your end
remembered you were
about to begin.
And find yourself.
Find yourself
in the adult world.
Find yourself
in the world
of responsibility,
laughter,
pain.

Your young years
now soaked in
mother's tears.
Mother not allowed
to watch you grow
from seedling
into flower.

The pain of parting
for good.
The pain of parting.
The pain.
The pain of mother's love
for daughter.
The pain of mother's love
The pain of love
remains a sharp edge
of your memory.

*

NAJMA KAZI

Definitions

*

An article entitled 'Maids and Madams' was submitted for publication to *Mukti*, an Asian women's publication, when *Mukti* first came into existence in 1982. The article highlighted the relationship between Indian 'madams' and their African maids in South Africa and came to light during the compilation of *Mukti* Issue 4, dealing with 'Work', in August 1985. A majority of the then *Mukti* collective decided that the article did not have a place in the 'Work' Issue. It would instead be considered for the Issue on 'Racism'. It seemed that all of a sudden racism could be compartmentalized as a separate entity, unrelated to other areas of our lives.

The following critique was prompted by that response. Both 'Maids and Madams' and my critique were eventually published in the 'Racism' Issue of *Mukti* in spring 1987.

Re the article 'Maids and Madams'.

I would like an urgent discussion of the issue of our own racism at the earliest opportunity. I continue to be very unhappy at the decision taken by the majority of the members of the *Mukti* Collective on Sunday 3rd August 1985, not to publish 'Maids and Madams' in the 'Work' Issue of *Mukti* and to only consider the article for Issue 6 on 'Racism'. I am not convinced or even mildly satisfied by any of the reasons given at that meeting against publishing the article.

The decisions made on that Sunday have in my eyes seriously undermined the credibility of the *Mukti* Collective to challenge racism within and outside our communities. Till now I was under the impression that the public challenging of racism and sexism was fundamental to our very existence. This obviously does not apply when it comes to our own racism.

For me the worst thing about that Sunday afternoon was that we sounded like a bunch of white liberals as we uncomfortably laboured out our clichés against publishing the article.

Cliché number 1: The time isn't right because of the current unrest in South Africa.

As if the African Black population cannot see for themselves the chasm that has always existed between them and us Asians since the early days of British/Boer colonialism when Gandhi and his Indian followers, in fighting the white-imposed Pass Laws, chose not to extend their solidarity to the indigenous African Black population of South Africa.

Let us not live under any illusions. When 'Maids and Madams' is published in *Mukti* it will only be the beginning of us confronting openly and acknowledging the part we Asians have played and continue to play in perpetuating white-dominated racism against African Black people and ultimately against ourselves. African Black people do not need *Mukti* to remind them of the way we Asians (excluding a few notable exceptions) have colluded with white people in perpetuating apartheid in South Africa. Indeed, today came the news of African Black attacks on the Indian community in Natal, ironically the very place where 'Maids and Madams' is set.

The Asian community in present-day South Africa is a very wealthy one and has, on the whole, chosen to remain 'apolitical' in the role of middle people as assigned to it by the white minority, instead of throwing in its lot with the majority African Black population. In the course of the revolutionary upheaval that is now sweeping across Southern Africa there may well be more attacks on Asians.

Where will *Mukti* stand then?

We are foolish to imagine that witholding the publishing of an article highlighting the relationship between African Black women workers and their Asian 'madams' will make one iota of a difference to this process.

Cliché number 2: Maids and madams exist in India, Pakistan etc, so suggesting that there is nothing extraordinary about the situation of Indian madams and their Black African maids in South Africa.

We all know that maids and madams continue to exist in India, Pakistan etc, but it is shameful when we use it as a justification for not coming to grips with our own racism.

We sounded just like many white people who, when confronted with their imperialism/racism, dismiss it on the grounds that the white working-classes, the Irish etc, were/are hard-done-by. They often maintain that our own oppression has little to do with white racism but all to do with the ruling classes who control power.

Shame on us for resorting to the same tactic.

Cliché number 3: White people will use the article against us to divide and rule and so widen the rift between us and African Black people.

Have we not always acknowledged that everything we publish in *Mukti* can be used against us as a community?

In *Mukti* Issue 2 (Family) we clearly stated that we were no longer prepared to use this threat as an excuse to leave unchallenged the sexism within our own community.

Yet now we find it so difficult to talk about and challenge the racism of our community towards African Black people.

Cliché number 4: 'Maids and Madams' will be considered *in a context* for the Issue on 'Racism'.

But I thought we agreed that since racism is for us a fundamental oppression, we could not evaluate any aspect of our lives such as the family, health, work, sexuality, without considering the effect racism has on that aspect. All our Issues have been about racism and sexism within the context of, say, the family, work, sexuality.

And 'Maids and Madams' is about our racism within the context of work, and it had a place in the 'Work' Issue.

What really depressed and upset me was that the *Mukti* collective, having decided that 'Maids and Madams' would be more appropriate for the 'Racism' Issue, was even then only prepared to consider the article for the Issue when the time came.

The article has to be 'in context' and we the *Mukti* collective would provide that 'context'.

I want to make it clear that for me, 'Maids and Madams' stands on its own and does not need a 'context' (whatever that means), particularly if it is to be considered for an Issue on 'Racism'.

The context is Racism.

I also want it understood that 'we' excludes me. I will not undertake to be part of providing that 'context'.

Let those women who feel the article needs a 'context' undertake that responsibility.

This talk of putting things in 'context' is also something many white people often talk about, when we confront them with their racism.

Shame on us for using the same tactic.

Some weeks ago some of us were upset that a Black women's group somewhere in London defined Black women as indigenous African women, and said that other non-white women such as Asian women were not welcome to their group. I was not sure what I felt then, but since Sunday's meeting I'm clear. I feel that the group are justified in taking the position they do.

We exposed our racism on Sunday and since we are not yet ready to deal with it, we have no place in a Black women's group. As our confusion over this article shows, our presence would only serve to increase the mistrust that already exists between Asian and indigenous African people.

The problem is that we forget who it is that we are supposed to be aiming *Mukti* at. *Mukti* is aimed at Asian women. And since our racism against indigenous African Black and indeed dark-skinned Black Asian people is, like sexism, part of our heritage, it is important for us to challenge this heritage through the pages of *Mukti*.

ZHANA

Fat

Marva dragged herself in from the November cold and panted her way up the stairs. Lately her body felt like lead, it took a huge effort to lift it. She'd just been to see an exhibition on ancient Nigerian art. The sculptures had struck her by their familiarity – particularly the fertility symbols. Bulging bellies, full breasts, round thighs and buttocks. Marva mentally hugged herself. The natural form was not only appreciated, but worshipped, in those days.

For once, she had not felt that her large body was oversized, ungainly, or out of place. For once, Marva had felt positively *normal.* But that feeling had not lasted. As Marva left the exhibition room, a white woman rudely pushed past her, as if she weren't even there. Marva called after her in a loud voice, 'Don't you know how to say "excuse me"?' The woman turned back to stare a stare which Marva could hear as clearly as if it were spoken: 'You had no right to be standing there anyway. You're taking up too much room on the planet.'

Marva shrugged her shoulders and moved away. Too much trouble to think about, the burden of the insult got stuffed into a pigeonhole deep in Marva's subconscious. She sighed and, feeling heavy, dragged herself home.

On the mat inside the front door, a letter bearing a US return address stared up at Marva. Sylvia and Marva had become friends when they were at college together in the States and, although time and distance had separated them, the two women still shared an emotional closeness.

The letter contained the usual gossip. Sylvia was worried, yet again, about failing her exams. It had taken her years to get into medical school, where she was studying to be a doctor. The professors at college had refused to give her good marks in a lot of the science subjects. She, like the other Black students, had been given a hard time, being made to repeat some essential biology and chemistry exams over and over. Marva remembered the time when one professor had advised Sylvia, 'Maybe you're not cut out to be a doctor.' Sylvia had just rolled her eyes, stood up and walked out of the tutorial. Marva remembered just wanting to scream abuse at him. His racism had been so glaring. But, of course, such things were not done at a genteel ladies' college.

Sylvia had started spending her summers at a Black university in her home town where, out from under the constraints of racism, she had taken advanced biology and chemistry subjects and done well enough in them to be admitted to medical school. Still struggling, she was determined to pass her exams.

Marva could hear Sylvia's voice as she read the letter.

> 'Girl, you know this diet is kickin' behind, but I've just *got* to lose some weight. I'm not like you, a few pounds really does show on me.'

Marva wondered where on her body Sylvia could possibly lose the weight from.

'I'm sitting on it, girl.'

Every time Sylvia put on weight, whichever man she was dating at the time wanted her to keep it on. 'You look good, girl. You look good!' he'd repeat with enthusiasm. Marva's mind would drift back to thoughts of the men lingering on pavements, staring after Sylvia as if they'd never seen buttocks before. Their eyes were drawn to her posterior magnetically. Sometimes they made rude comments, more often just stared. Sylvia, whose mind was perhaps caught in the same drift, would announce, 'I've gotta lose some weight.'

The letter continued.

'You should lose some weight, too. I'm not just nagging, you know. I really worry about you. It's not good for your heart, carrying around all that extra weight.'

Marva got up to put her dinner in the oven. Walking through the flat, she caught her reflection in a mirror, and had to fight a sense of disgust. Jeans and a pullover did not flatter her nineteen stones. 'Clothes should fit bodies, people shouldn't have to fit into clothes,' she thought, but as well as she knew this with her head, she didn't believe it in her heart.

It was the same old story. Lose weight, slim down, reduce. We're telling you this for your own good, you know. After twelve years of struggling to fit into a size 12, of feeling guilty when she gave in to her craving for 'naughty' foods, of wasting money on slimming magazines, diet books, and low-calorie foods, Marva had finally started to accept that her large body suited her needs. 'I'm just not prepared to put so much energy into all that pain, into holding myself back, into suppressing, rather than *expressing*, myself!', she decided. But no one wanted to hear that.

'If anything gives me heart trouble, it will be the good intentions of all my friends and relations,' Marva thought. But still she couldn't honestly look into the mirror and say she *loved* her body with the kind of loving care and respect the artists who had carved the fertility statues had poured into their work. Marva sometimes felt that if she could get acceptance, let alone love, from the people around her, perhaps she could begin to accept herself.

Marva continued to read the letter. Sylvia was back on the Pill, which she used to regulate her periods. No more pregnancy scares! Marva shuddered. There must be a better way. Pouring all those chemicals into your body – ugh! 'You're studying to be a doctor – you should know better,' Marva remarked aloud. She grabbed a pen, went running into the other room, opened her desk drawer and rummaged frantically for some paper. She found some, sat down and started to scribble:

> Dear Sylvia. I *had* to write to you. You'll probably think *I'm* 'just nagging'. Even so, I must send you a copy of an article I saved for you about the latest report on the negative effects of the Pill – yet again. They tested those things on Puerto Rican women, originally.

> (You should know that.) Used them as guinea pigs. God knows what kind of side effects they're keeping secret, or didn't even bother to test for. We probably won't find out for another twenty years! Please, don't keep putting that shit in your body.

The next morning, Marva was walking down the hill to the tube station when one of her neighbours, a Black woman of about fifty-five, waved and called out a greeting to her. 'When's the baby due?' she asked, smiling. Marva waved back, 'I'm not having one.' The woman continued to smile. 'Maybe she doesn't believe me,' thought Marva. The disapproval she was so used to encountering did not glint in the woman's eye. 'How odd. I suppose she expects me to feel embarrassed.'

At work, the women in the office carried on their daily conversation about diets and slimming. 'I know I shouldn't have this,' Karen intoned, raising some forbidden goodie to her lips. 'According to whom?', Marva wondered to herself. 'I want to lose 5 lbs,' Karen continued. Marva could not even visualize a loss so miniscule. She had no idea what it would mean – 5 lbs either way certainly wouldn't show on her own body. From which part of the anatomy did one lose 5 lbs? How could anyone get so excited about such a small loss of weight?

The women made no attempt to include Marva in their talk of what they should and should not be eating, how guilty they felt at indulging their greedy desires. She was obviously beyond redemption. There was no point in even entering into a discussion with someone who had so utterly and drastically transgressed. So a wasteland of silence existed between Marva and the other women on the subject of weight. Occasionally, an intrepid one would venture across the barrier, tentatively offering Marva a line. 'I'm so fat,' she would say, glancing hopefully at Marva, waiting for a sympathetic reply. Marva would merely smile bemusedly. There was nothing she could do with such a line. To utter her true feelings, that the woman was no more fat than nine feet tall, would leave the woman feeling unsupported and unsatisfied, but to agree would be dishonest. So she said nothing.

On this particular day, Marva was glad to be left out of the conversation. She was lost in her own thoughts. The article kept creeping back into her mind, and she felt angry. All those growths appearing all over women's bodies because they'd chosen not to have children, because they'd wanted the convenience of being able to pop a tiny white pill into their mouths once a day and become removed, as men were removed, from the threat of unwanted pregnancy. Because they'd wanted to enjoy sex, enjoy pleasure, their bodies, men, without having an eight-pound bouncing consequence to deal with nine months later. This was what they'd bought. Suffering, death. They'd exchanged one growth in the body for another.

Marva didn't always remember the day she'd found out her sister had fibroids. Jennifer had been in pain month in, month out, doubled over in pain with her periods, lying in bed in agony. There was nothing the doctors could do for her, except offer to cut the problem out. A few convenient cuts, the whole messy business could be performed through the vagina, there would be no scars. Well, no external scars. Marva remembered receiving the phonecall from her mother. Jennifer was in the hospital, she was having a hysterectomy. She didn't want to have any kids. And Marva thought, 'Good, I'm glad she's made her decision, I'm relieved that she can get what she wants.' But still, waking up in the middle of the night, she thought, 'I wonder if my sister's all right. It's a very simple operation, but I wonder if she'll be all right.' And wondered, just a little, in the back of her mind, whether it was entirely necessary.

Marva didn't always think about the times Sylvia had woken up in the night, back in the house they'd shared as students. The dreams that always meant something. Sylvia knew when her aunt was going to lose a breast, when her mother would lose two breasts. Sylvia ringing up another aunt, long-distance. 'She's going to have a biopsy.' Sylvia always knew beforehand that the test would prove positive.

Marva occasionally remembered the time the doctor at the Family Planning Association told her that, if she couldn't remember to take her pill, she could always have the injection. She remembered the fear, the sense of wanting to throw on her clothes and run, as fast and as far as she could, from that place, from the people who could take total control over her body and her chances for future offspring. She remembered the helplessness and the fear, but what they left behind was anger.

Today, Marva remembered all of these incidents. The article had triggered memories which, one by one, paraded into her mind. She felt angry and was grateful for the buzzing voices of the women in their meaningless conversations, glad they were too preoccupied to read her thoughts as she could so clearly read theirs. The women walked around Marva today when they met in the corridor or the lift or the loo. They thought it was pity they felt for her, who had let her weight get so out of control. They thought they held her in contempt for having so little willpower. But Marva could read the fear on their faces and in their minds. 'I am the embodiment of their worst fears,' she thought. 'They're terrified of ending up like me.'

Marva had not planned to attend the conference on women's reproductive rights that weekend, but now every cell in her body drew her towards it. She belonged at that conference. That was where her body had to be that weekend.

Marva walked out into a bright, golden Saturday morning and headed towards the bus stop. She felt tense, anticipatory, yet determined. Although she wasn't sure what to expect from the conference, her sense of purpose felt good.

At the bus stop, a middle-aged Black woman looked Marva up and down. There was no sense of greeting. Although Marva returned her look, the woman would not meet her eyes, but at the same time did not seem to be able to stop staring at Marva's midriff. When the bus came, Marva climbed onto it, feeling unnerved.

She arrived at the conference to encounter a sea of white faces, speckled here and there with Black. The agenda was already filled – it seemed the day was to be devoted to 'reproductive technology', devices and procedures which Marva found uninspiring. 'This is all well and good,' she thought, as the speakers droned on, 'but when are they going to start talking about people and people's needs?' One white woman spoke about genetic engineering, about being able to choose one's baby. Marva found this approach offensive. She thought the topic carried overtones of creating a master race. However, at no point did the speaker raise this problem. After the presentation, an Asian woman from the audience stood up and challenged the speaker and, with her, the organizers of the conference. 'The main concern for Black women all over the world is to have healthy babies and see them survive,' she stated. Marva applauded. Then, she heard white women around her start to grumble. Apparently, the Asian woman had been challenging speakers all morning. A few of the white women in the audience actually shouted and booed, and one called the Asian woman a 'trouble-maker'. Marva was shocked and appalled at this response. Once again, a single woman was being scapegoated for speaking out. Marva decided she had to talk to the woman, to make contact with her and offer her support. During the tea break, she went up to her and they started chatting. 'I'm so glad you made that point about Black women's priorities,' Marva stated. 'That speaker didn't mention anything that had to do with our needs.'

'There isn't even one Black or Asian woman on the panel,' the woman replied.

Two other Black women came up to the pair. The Asian woman, whose name was Meena, suggested that they meet that afternoon, during the time set aside for workshops. They all agreed. As Marva commented, 'There's nothing going on here for us, anyway.'

That afternoon, something wonderful occurred. All the Black women came together in an impromptu workshop. Although it had not been planned, they all found they had a great deal of information and experience to share. An American Indian woman refugee from the United States, living in France, told of how she felt having her life in danger, having to duck regularly in and out of cars to avoid the CIA agents who were pursuing her. The discussion brought up development issues about women in African countries trying to keep their children alive, while being told to feed them powdered milk they could not afford. About women in the Pacific who, due to years of nuclear testing on their land, were giving birth to jelly-like substances – women who would be glad to have a living child, and who weren't particularly bothered about if it were missing an arm or a leg. Marva met a group of women who were campaigning against the dispensing of the injectable contraceptive, Depoprovera. She felt really inspired. At last there was a productive channel for her anger.

In the plenary that afternoon, white women complained because 'all the Black women had gone off by themselves'. Marva was not prepared for the level of hostility that was directed against them. The white women started complaining that an 'unscheduled' workshop had been formed. Marva stood up to speak in response to this criticism.

'You're treating us like naughty little girls. I think you're pissed off because we don't want to address your agenda. Well, your agenda isn't speaking to us. Black women are here today to deal with real issues, life and death issues that are affecting us, and you don't want to know. You lot really don't have a clue. Well, until you start listening to us, we don't want anything to do with you, you have nothing to offer Black women.' All the Black women, and some of the white ones, applauded. Marva picked up her coat and walked out of the hall, followed by the Black women participants and the white participants who supported their action. Marva's knees were shaking. She couldn't believe she'd said those things. But she had.

Marva left the conference feeling uplifted and inspired, yet angry at the way the Black women's concerns had been marginalized. Later, as she boarded the bus, exhausted, she tried to keep her balance as she pushed past people and their shopping, avoiding stepping on toes. As she squeezed into a seat, Marva felt resentment from a pair of eyes denying her right to take up so much room on the bus. She turned and looked the white woman sitting behind her squarely in the eye. 'I'll take up as much room as I like,' Marva thought, settling comfortably into her seat.

ZHANA

For Tyra

I once knew a Black woman
Who had a son
In an all-white town.
When a white woman called him
Black bastard,
She kicked the woman's ass
Up and down the street
All over town.
The boy will grow up knowing
His Blackness,
His body,
His mind,
Are worth fighting for.

Tyra's mother, why?
Why did you let a man
Kill your beautiful Black daughter?
Could you not bear to see
A replica of yourself
Survive?
You were not there for her
When she was being
Bitten
To death;
Why do you visit her murderer?
I think it's because
The image of you reflected
In his eyes
Fills your burning, deperate need
To reaffirm
Your self-hate.

Ports of Call

*

Whenever we talk about our experience in this country, white people start creeping in, racism infiltrates the conversation. We don't seem to be able to 'be' without it. We would not be *here* without it – racism is central to our experience of being in Britain and permeates, at some level, every transaction we engage in.

Having said that, the situation is not as grim as that statement would seem to imply. Black women are nothing if not survivors. We daily confront the injustices that threaten us; our continued existence is, in itself, a triumph over the forces of oppression. Out of the wreckage of the human condition, we have salvaged lives which are more or less intact. We continue to function, to define ourselves on our own terms. We continue to make those difficult decisions that determine the course of our lives as we wish to steer them.

DEBJANI CHATTERJEE

Animal Regalia

'For the launch of our modest exhibition,
we need an expert on animal regalia,'
announced the enthusing gallery person.
'Just a small audience, only local media –
you volunteered to make a contribution –
even ten minutes on animal regalia
from you will sound authentic, gain attention,
and spiced snacks can be ordered from the Light of Asia,'
purred the telephone voice in expectation.
I longed to plead a sudden total amnesia.
Well, I work in community relation,
so you think me a walking encyclopedia
on saris, surma, steel bands, circumcision,
calypso, kosher, carnival bacchanalia,
reggae, ragas, Rastas, race, revolution,
multi-culturalese, sickle cell anaemia,
equal opportunities, deportation,
halal meat, Hinduism, hunger, third world hernia,
visas, arranged marriages, immigration,
ethnic monitoring and paraphernalia.
I should be used now to this phenomenon,
but confessed surprise at animal regalia,
and duly pleaded lack of all connection.
'But elephants, horses, camels come from India,
just like you!' came the logical assumption.
Well, so they do. I begin to get the idea!

JUDITH KAURMEKELI GREENIDGE

Untitled Story

Lying on her bed, Shirley groaned in agony at the pain that crawled inside her. Her slender body had grown thinner from lack of nourishment and from the constant torment that the people in the institute were giving her. Night and day she was repeatedly force-fed with drugs. She was made to sit for hours in a tiny room with a man in a white coat. He would probe her every now and again, as some specimen ready to be experimented on. His sarcastic remarks bruised her and all she felt able to do was to scream and scream.

The pain was growing worse and worse, yet she was soon becoming used to it, watching and waiting for the time when that little white door would open and two Black women dressed in new white uniforms would enter and prepare for the battle of force-feeding her. Striving hard to push aside the pain, Shirley turned to the comforting memories of her elder sister Maureen, who for five years had been living in Barbados as a successful writer with her seven-year-old son, Tafferi. Shirley smiled a long smile as she recalled the day the letter arrived inviting her to spend two glorious months with her sister. Oh, how the sun hit her before the plane had even landed, and the long shrill sound of her name being called out which met her at the airport.

The two sisters embraced as if they had met for the first time, tightly holding on to all those damned years that had separated them, and yet within that instant those years had been quickly discarded.

'So it is now we finally meet!' greeted Maureen, still holding on tightly to her sister's hand. They embraced once more while tears filled their eyes.

'It's been a long time,' Shirley muttered.
'Far too long.'
As they stood together in the glorious hot sunshine, Shirley was filled with so much emotion. Seeing her sister again after all this time brought back so many memories and made her feel a deep sense of relief. Standing back, Shirley took a good look at Maureen; she had grown beautifully, her face hadn't changed much but she sure looked stunning in her new look and expensive clothes. Shirley thought it would take all her week's wages to pay for one of Maureen's suits.
Maureen laughed while remembering something from their past and said, 'You can borrow my clothes this time, when my back's turned.' They smiled at this thought, which was a joke now but when they were growing up had been a serious problem between them. Maureen used to take Shirley's good church clothes and go out partying with her friends, then return them in a terrible state, which always annoyed Shirley, but no matter how she tried to hide her good clothes her sister always found them.
They were not alike these two, in fact they were so different it was quite surprising how they managed to stay the best of friends despite this obvious difference.
Throughout Shirley's two months stay in Barbados she felt so alive and good to be with her sister again. They laughed, cried and shared many memories of the past. Maureen's son, Tafferi, enjoyed his aunt's company and liked hearing the stories about his mother. Shirley always felt sad that he had grown up not really knowing his mother's sister, and her not really being there to watch him grow up, but they were together now through God's mercy and she had no intention of wasting time pondering over the past.
During her stay she visited many of Maureen's friends and went to big luncheons and dinner parties for the launch of her sister's new book. Shirley was so proud of her sister becoming famous with her writing career. She never realized before how successful Maureen had become. At parties she found herself proudly telling people that Maureen and she were sisters.
The saddest part of the whole holiday was having to leave

Maureen and return home. They went to a party on the last night and stayed up all night, drinking and talking. The tension was in the atmosphere. Maureen kept wandering around the house; it was obvious that she had been crying and that she was trying desperately not to let it show. Maureen went up to Shirley and hugged her tightly and said, 'I know it's going to be a long time before we get to see each other again.'

'No, no, it's your turn to come and see me,' Shirley uttered, trying not to make her sister too upset. Tafferi sat in the front part of the house and shouted out, 'Don't go, Aunty, we want you to stay with us.' Shirley laughed a little, went to hug him and burst into tears at the same time.

The airport scene brought about more tears. As Shirley's flight was called out, she went around hugging and kissing all her friends and relatives; they were terribly sad to see her go. Tafferi held on to her hand all the time she waited there. She felt like a queen with the flowers and presents that were given to her.

Passing through the passport barrier, Shirley turned to wave her final goodbye. Maureen was pressed up against the glass barrier, tears streaming down her face.

'I love you, sis, please write and phone me,' cried Maureen. 'Take care of your sweet self.'

'Bye, Aunty, come back soon,' Tafferi shouted, as they watched Shirley disappear amongst the other passengers ready to board the plane . . .

The opening of the little white door invaded her reverie. Christ, so soon, she thought, but dared not utter a word. It seemed only minutes since she had had her last dose of medicine. Her mind became distorted and confused, a sudden violent urge erupted in the pits of her stomach.

'No more, no more, leave me alone!' she screamed frantically.

'Grab her arms – so she playing up again?'

Shirley stopped struggling, she became passive and strangely distant, as if suddenly she had no control or care of her actions.

'Give me the tablet,' she heard herself whisper, to the amazement of the two women. There's no use in fighting it, she thought, they'll win in the end, they always do.

The patients were allowed occasionally to walk around the hospital and view their prison. Slow, weary bodies dragged themselves around in gleaming white robes, searching into cupboards, looking under tables. The place was either loud and noisy or else too quiet, the atmosphere thick with tension. At such times it was inevitable that something was about to happen. Not a soul dared question the reason for the tension – it was accepted – but no sooner had that solemness evaporated than the place became electrified. It was then the time to watch out for the trouble that was usually to follow.

Polished white table-tops shone to the reflection of the sun streaming through the grilled windows. Cool cream carpet ran for miles upon miles along the perfectly painted white corridors. Everything was in order, not one scratch fossilized itself within the depths of the furniture. The inhabitants knew the rules and they stuck rigidly to them. In some rooms, patients sat and chatted quietly, while in other rooms they played little IQ tests simply out of habit, or boredom.

Could all these people be mad? Was it possible to categorize all these loosely innocent people as mentally insane? Who had that authority, who had the right to sit in his plush office miles away from reality where, every minute of the day, people were crying out in desperation for comfort and love, for someone to sit and listen to their troubles? How could he know anything of human suffering, of such sheer loneliness that one's mind suddenly stops functioning and gives in? He swivels around in his plush office chair, takes one quick glance and with one flick of his hand consigns another unfortunate soul to a faster way to insanity. All these thoughts came flooding into Shirley's mind as she sat tightly in her chair, restraining herself from leaping up and scratching the eyes out of the nearest doctor in charge. Surely I'm not insane, how can I be? I can think and make clear judgements in my mind, how can they say I am mad 'cause me kill that bastard of a husband?

Shirley caught sight from the corner of her eye of one of the nurses staring at her. The woman quickly shifted position uncomfortably in her chair when Shirley caught her looking.

Heartbeats fast and long drummed against Shirley's chest, sweat encircled her neck and armpits. Her throat had expanded two inches and her stomach was cursing her for having put it through so much tension and nervousness.

'So, Mrs . . .' paused the deep-sounding voice, while fidgetty hands fumbled with some loose paper in a file. Shirley watched this man with some amusement in her deep-set eyes: ain't he a joke, she thought to herself.

'Yes, Mrs Andrews . . . I see from this file that you had a nasty accident with your husband.'

'I don't recall no accident,' she replied, allowing the word accident to linger on her lips a while.

'Uhm, yes,' came the mechanical voice again.

'Why did you do it – kill him, I mean?'

Shirley paused for a while. Was there any point in answering this dumb-assed man, she thought. Whatever I say won't get me out of this place, it's only for their record, another case to file away in their chests upon chests of documents on patients that they gave up on or that they didn't bother with in the first place.

'Men are trouble from the day they born, they never let up on us women.' This is what Ma always said. She would sit in her chair, with her family around, after they had finished their supper. Then she'd laugh out loudly, reminiscing of her encounters with the no-good men she knew and loved over the years gone by.

This mood was familiar to those who were close her. Her youngest son, Courtney, always prepared the little table beside Ma's chair, with a bottle of rum and ice-cold water for the older folk to drink, while the young ones drank pop or juicy.

They sat up till all hours of the morning, with their talk and high laughter. It was a kind of ritual that took place upon an evening. The Godards would pop in for a drink as they always did and occasionally the neighbours from beyond the house would show up as well. Everyone talked about so-and-so woman run off with she husband's best friend from St Michael's and left the children with their father, or how the young boy from down town was drowned in the sea a few days back.

These talks were always high-spirited and usually ended when Ma could talk no more for tiredness or when she felt lick up with the rum. It was then they started to head for home. The children had long gone to bed and the cattle now brought into the back yard, everyone went to sleep.

Shirley couldn't help drifting back to the past every now and again. It was comforting for her to think of her mum, how she was a strong woman, so determined. She was loved by everyone. She had her awkward ways but people cared for her and understood her.

Ma warned me against marrying this man I called my husband. She told me he was no good, and take it from her 'cause she knew what she was talking about.

'Shirl, I tell you, girl, that man ain't no good for you.' Ma was persistent.

'Ma, he's not like that now, he's real serious on me, he wants to take care of me.'

'I tell ya, chil, I seen that man walking the street with so many women hanging pon he arm, like he can't stand up by himself.' Ma was serious in her speech, but knew her daughter had no intention of taking her advice.

'What wrong with that good-looking man that you was talking to at church last Sunday?' Ma went on.

'Oh, Ma, he was just saying hello, there's nothing in that.'

Ma didn't bother with Shirl no more, it was too late to change her mind. In a way Ma was really making sure that her daughter knew what she wanted and that she was happy with her choice. She shook her head disappointedly to herself as she watched Shirl hanging out the clothes on the line.

'If only my mother talked to me when I fell for that fool fool man, Anderson, I would not have got myself into the mess I did, bringing up the children and working night and day by myself,' Ma thought out aloud . . .

Shirley shook back to reality. I had better get out of this rocking chair and prepare some food for the others, she thought to herself. Somehow she couldn't pull herself away. Shirley looked around the house. It was sure in a bad way. After all this time it seemed strange to be back here again.

Sunlight was seeping through the windows that faced her, reflecting tiny shapes of leaves on to the wall. Everything was just how she left it that day. A day she cared not to bring to mind again. To stop the oncoming thoughts, Shirley turned her body to look around the room. The plants were no more. They had dried up and disappeared into the dry soil.

Over in the corner the sewing machine stood and the same material was draped over the side waiting for her to return and finish it off. The sofa that acted as a divider between the living room and the kitchen had gathered piles of dust. The calendar, still opened at the month of July '76, was hanging over on the wall above the mantlepiece.

Shirley looked over into the kitchen. The drawer below the sink was still opened. Tears rolled freely down her face. Memories were forcing their way back and she could not help but cry. The nausea she was feeling now was making her stomach turn and she rose and ran up to the bathroom where she was sick over the toilet.

The house was too quiet for Shirley. After she had wandered around the bedrooms she came back downstairs and went into the front room, which was the coolest and neatest part of the house. Photographs of her children were placed over the fireplace and on the small table sitting in the middle of the room. Taking one of the photos, she kissed the three children who smiled back at her. They were older now and would be with her very soon.

A feeling of strength washed over Shirley's body and caused her to feel dizzy. Sitting down, Shirley saw the family photo-album lying under the table. Bending down to pick it up she felt her heart beating fast. She turned the pages and suddenly stopped. There he was on their wedding day. He was so handsome-looking, especially with that smile he was so famous for.

'I loved you, man,' Shirley whispered as she stroked the

picture. 'But now I am free of you, you can't hurt me anymore. I am stronger now because of you and I will be happy.'

Shirley stood up and went back into the other room and sat back in the rocking chair.

The sun outside was scorching hot, it was the middle of summer. Waves of dry heat swarmed the air leaving tired, restless people to survive the long days of summer that were still to come. Loud laughter and screams of children were heard as they played in the streets until their hearts were content.

Walking along Bellware View, with its beautiful tall elegant trees swaying gently to the hot breeze, it was easy to spot the medium-sized family house standing alone on the corner. The house looked no different from the other houses along that way, except that all the windows and doors were shut tight as if one early morning the owners had got up and fled from home. Not a single thing stirred. Through the curtainless window Shirley could be seen sitting, rocking back and forth at a calm steady pace. Her face was aglow as beautiful thoughts of her daughter came flooding back. A smile could be seen forming on her small round face.

Shirley's daughter Evenlyn was her first child by the man she fell in love with and hoped to marry, but this dream was soon shattered when he told her he was too young to marry and that he wanted to start his career and settle down later. When she told him that she was pregnant with his child, he ordered her to get rid of it. Despite this, Shirley kept the child, against objections from her mother and the rest of the family that they could not afford to have a baby in the family.

Some months later Shirley married a man from her parish and emigrated to England, leaving her baby daughter behind in Barbados with her mother. After eight years Shirley had enough money to send for her daughter and that was when the trouble with having her daughter brought up by a man other than her natural father began to emerge.

Shirley would boast of how well Evenlyn was doing at school and how she always came first in her subjects. Evenlyn grew older; people couldn't tell whether the two were sisters or just friends. They went everywhere together, shopping, dances, and Evenlyn was always helping her mother with her study work for evening classes. On evenings she would give the little ones their supper and put them to bed, as well as having to do her college work.

There was always that tight atmosphere in the house whenever Shirley's husband, Kenneth, was around and Evenlyn was not in her room studying. Although he said he accepted her, he still kept her at a distance. There were times Shirley recalled when he spited her by not allowing her to have the extra food or the pocket money he gave to the others.

Even though it upset Shirley to see these things happening, she had to satisfy herself that this was the only way for her daughter to continue living with them.

Every week there were arguments of one kind or another. Kenneth accusing Shirley of being a whore and that she was encouraging Evenlyn to do the same by going out to parties with her. There was one occasion when Shirley and her daughter returned home late from a party with friends, to find that their front door was locked from the inside. After trying for what seemed like hours to wake the children asleep inside, they had to resort to calling the police. When the police arrived, Kenneth argued that he must have fallen asleep with the latch on the door. Angrily Shirley went to sleep in the children's bedroom, because she was too scared to sleep with Kenneth in the state he was in. Huddled up in one of the kids' beds now, Shirley felt safe to sleep. Later she woke to the slamming of her bedroom door; as she propped herself up to see what was happening, Kenneth poured a pan of cold water on to her, leaving her drenched and very shaken. She was pregnant with her youngest and only son at the time.

Ever since Shirley could remember, she always warned and protected her children against the 'evil of men' as she called it, even her husband. She made a point of explaining to them not to let anyone mess around or touch them in a way they didn't like, and especially told Evenlyn as she was the oldest. When Shirley was admitted into hospital to give birth to her last baby, she sent Evenlyn to her cousin's house for the week.

Shirley recalled that when Evenlyn was fourteen years old, they would have a lot of fights for what seemed very trivial things. It was as if something deep troubled both of them but neither dared say what it was, which hurt Shirley a great deal because she was so used to them sharing their problems. There were times when Shirley found herself beating her daughter more and more but her husband, instead of helping the situation, only made it worse by backing up Evenlyn. This torment went on for a long time and Shirley regretted the day that she didn't sign the divorce papers when she had the chance to do so. What finally convinced her of the thoughts that plagued her mind was when she returned home one afternoon after a late-night shift to hear Evenlyn shouting at Kenneth to get out of her room and not to trouble her again, otherwise she would tell Mum. For some reason Shirley had always known what her husband was up to but she had no proof and really did not want to believe it. That night when she was lying in bed she asked him if what she thought was true, knowing full well that he would never admit to it. He turned to her and said, 'If I was going to do anything you would not even know,' and he rolled over and went to sleep.

All night Shirley lay awake thinking of ways to destroy this man who lay beside her. She thought to poison him or stab him or something, so long as he didn't live anymore. She felt sick in her stomach and questioned herself over and over again as to why Evenlyn would do such a thing, but she couldn't bring herself to discuss it with her.

Life was not the same, Shirley and Evenlyn were growing further and further apart. Evenlyn studied hard at college for her A-levels and was soon ready to go out into the world of work. Things remained the same for Shirley; she too continued to study for her fashion course, but part-time, and worked while her three little ones were at school. Shirley learnt to take things as they came, to put the past behind her and continue living her life as she had always done. Yet in her mind she blamed Evenlyn for everything because she had thought they were close enough to trust each other and she was wrong. Even though Shirley knew that it was her responsibility to do something when she heard Evenlyn shouting at her husband, Kenneth, to leave her alone. Still, Shirley could not help putting the blame on her daughter. She felt very hurt and betrayed, especially after she had constantly explained to Evenlyn that if this sort of thing should happen, she must approach her mother about it. Her husband had succeeded in taking away the most precious thing in her life and that was her love for her first child, Evenlyn. Now that was violated and the stain could never be erased . . .

The rocking chair that Shirley was sitting in had come to a halt. The expression on her face was no longer one of delight, but one of sadness and hate. The sun had gone down now and it was getting late. A whole hour had gone past while Shirley sat and allowed her mind to drift wheresoever it desired. She felt stiff from sitting for so long in that chair and so she got up and wandered over to the kitchen. Putting the kettle on she noticed how overgrown the garden had become. The children loved to play out there till all hours of the night, she thought to herself. Even though it was still hot and very stuffy Shirley was unaware of the sweat that had formed above her lip and on her forehead; the thick woollen jumper she was wearing didn't help much either.

The hot cup of tea warmed her inside and made her feel good. Shirley walked over to the sink where the drawer was left opened and closed it. This was the first time she had touched that drawer since the day everything happened. Stepping back from the sink, Shirley noticed the white marking on the tiled floor, which had lined the body of her husband where he fell.

In two quick flashes it was over, it was done. The gun found its way towards the floor beside the corpse. Silence like death itself engulfed the whole room. It swirled through every crack and rested finally upon its victim. Its victim – a middle-aged woman, short and slim, whose black body trembled with horror and shock at her own misfortune which now lay motionless upon the cold, hard floor. Never to awake, never to haunt and twist her mind like some undying disease tearing away at her brain. Whatever was to be the outcome of this incident, she had no care to know because what she had wanted to do for years was finally done.

The house, too, seemed relieved with this woman, as if it was silently seeking revenge upon that no-good-for-nothing lout. The man, her husband, whose lean body reeked with the same filth that it itself had contained. Whose body at one minute stormed and cursed the house and its members and the next walked the streets like a gentle tramp with all the pride and respectability of a holy man. He worked day in and day out, always sticking to his long-handed-down tradition of punctuality. Moaning and grumbling to himself about the matrimonial ceremony he to this day wished he'd never got himself involved in.

Shirley slowly lowered herself down next to the body and looked into his eyes – his dark brown eyes which left not one trace of remorsefulness but some glint of succeeding – that even though dead, he was still winning, still fighting the game to the bitter end. The game that was to lead her to the edge of insanity.

'Why did you kill him?' the doctor asked again.

'I was provoked,' she said, deciding to play his game, for the record.

'Uhm, I see . . .'

'You see what? Why are there so many Black patients in here?' Shirley shouted, pounding her fist on the table. This time the voice didn't bother to answer, instead it rambled on about how unusually unalike the other patients Shirley seemed.

'From this file it seems that you are quite . . .' his voice trailed off back into his neat but disordered file, each word swallowed up by the word that followed, cancelling them out, making them meaningless. Shirley stared off at the wall ahead. Her face was hot and sweaty, her eyes transfixed.

Blood, hot, sweat, panic. 'Scream, damn you, scream.' Hate, anger, pain – oh, the pain.

'Mummy, Mummy.' Floods of tears, hot sticky tears like lava licking up the wounds that it had itself created. Violence burning up inside, burning, eating, gnawing away at her womb, making her skin crawl, like burning flesh peeling off a body in flames.

Frustration beating away every nerve ending, sparking off daggers of contempt to pierce his sinful soul.

He raped her, my own flesh and blood. My own baby. He stuck his filthy prick inside her and destroyed her, violated her, scarred her for life. She was fourteen at the time, God knows how many times he did it to her. When I found out, my head swam, I cried for days on end. I thought I was going mad mad mad. Tears searched their way down Shirley's face as she recalled the day that she first swore to take revenge. Ever since, she had been living as she was now – surviving, because there was nothing else to do. She had been to see a regular psychiatrist but there was nothing he could do for her. She took valium to spare the endless agony at night but it was there, implanted as much in her mind as her daughter's.

'. . . These are therefore the reasons why you will have to remain here until something else can be resolved . . .' came that cold but calm mechanical voice, droning on monotonously, without a single care.

Shirley shook with the last thought of her poor little daughter, standing in the doorway of the dining room, screaming hysterically, screaming out for warm arms and breasts to come and wash the hurt and pain away.

Dazed and somewhat shaken from her recent thoughts, Shirley stood up and left the tiny white room and its filing cabinets. Her heart was heavy, she felt weak and faint.

'Be careful with yourself, woman, you look ready to fall,' came a sudden hard Black woman's voice from behind her. When Shirley turned around, it was the face of that stern-looking woman who was caught glancing at her from the other side of the lounge earlier that day. Somehow that voice didn't fit that face, she was a plump woman, small with a roundish, hard face, yet her eyes held all the warmth and love that was locked away inside of her.

'No, I'm fine,' Shirley said with a faint smile.

'Sure you are, look ya knees nearly touching the ground.' The woman smiled. 'So how you come to be here, then?' she inquired, handing Shirley a cup of hot chocolate.

Shirley, taken aback by such a direct question, especially from one of the staff, looked up suddenly and stared hard into the young woman's face. It was as stern and hard as before, allowing no emotion to show, as if that came from years of experience.

'I killed my husband,' she mumbled, not once allowing her eyes to leave the face of the strange woman who stood before her.

'Say, what he did to you, girl?' There was no hesitation in her voice, she spoke as if it was the normal thing to do. No sign of astonishment lurked within the cold kitchen that the two women were talking in. As if too heavy with disbelief, Shirley's head drooped forward and she gave an enormous long sigh of relief.

'Don't worry, child, you're not the first. There are many women who secretly wish they'd had the guts to do the same thing.' She paused as if in a dream all of her own. 'That's what some of these lot are in here for.' The woman laughed a hurtful sarcastic laugh. 'They went mad 'cause they didn't have enough guts and you're in here 'cause you did. Look girl, I gone, ya hear.'

The kitchen no longer seemed cold, it even had a homely look to it, even though all the walls were covered in glossy white paint. Could she be for real, thought Shirley? Man, I need to get out of here, I need to breathe.

After that brief encounter with the young Black woman, Shirley began to gather the strength to fight the days that were ahead of her. While she lay in her bed at nights she thought of nothing else but writing a letter to her sister in Barbados. The days grew longer and the itch to tell someone was becoming unbearable.

There was an unusual unpleasantness seeping through the white walls of the institute, as if slight murmurs were being suffocated around the rooms. Rain added no brightness to the eerie place. Dark clouds drifted overhead, waiting for the signal to burst open and pour all their contents upon the already condemned place. For some reason the wards of the hospital were suddenly infested with more staff – they buzzed about, hurriedly looking in and out of all the rooms as if searching, searching for some unknown thing to suddenly jump out at them.

Marica, the young round Black woman, sat upright in her armchair plaiting one of the other Black women's hair. Shirley thought she looked so engrossed with what she was doing that it seemed unfair to disturb her, yet she did. 'Marica!' she whispered. She had decided that today was the day that she would tell Marica about the letter. The letter she had pondered over for weeks in her mind, so much that she was ready to dictate it to her. 'Marica!' called Shirley again more forcefully. Marica raised her small plump body out of the armchair; she stood as if in a daze, and gazed wide-eyed around the room. Checking that no one was paying attention to what she was doing, she moved towards the kitchen in a very strange manner.

White uniforms floated around the rooms, still checking and keeping everything in order. Everyone's mind was occupied with whatever they were doing. The rain too, which had now come, had its part to play. It trickled slightly at first, then suddenly heavier drops bounced themselves off of the newly clean windows. Tiny glass bubbles formed neatly along the edge of the window sill and plunged lightly to the ground below.

'You haven't heard of the talk going around this place, girl?'

'No,' Shirley replied inquisitively, but yet eager to tell of her latest idea.

'A Black woman was found hanged in she room last night, ain't no one know the reason why. The girl at peace now, God rest her soul.' Marica rolled her eyes to the ceiling then returned them to Shirley. Shirley's eyes bulged at the horrific news, for a time things seemed to go blank, nothing was registering properly. How could this be? she questioned herself silently. Fear dug its claws into her throat and clung on tight to her heart. When was this? Who found her? Does anyone here know her? All these questions hammered her mind, drilling a neat little hole in the middle of her head. All she was able to do was to turn and walk away.

'So what was it you wanted, Shirley?' The voice trailed on as if it had gone straight past Shirley and down the long white corridor to the place where the woman, another woman, a victim, had swung lifeless back and forth, high in her room. Shirley kept on walking, oblivious to the strained voice of Marica who stood baffled with hands on hips. She kept walking, blinded by the words that were tearing away inside her, blinded by the thoughts that it could just as well have been her swinging, swinging, not caring, praying to die, praying to be rid of this constant torment that was awaiting her every single minute of her life, while every single second drove her just that bit more insane. As she began to turn the corridor, Shirley heard faint sobbing in the distance behind her and she turned her head to see the big plump woman, sobbing sobbing against the wall. Her face no longer stern, her eyes no longer glowed with the love and warmth that was buried deep within her, she sobbed like a new born baby sucking in its first breath of air to survive but to survive she had no desire to do.

Once back in her room, Shirley remembered the letter she had wanted to tell Marica about, those weeks of planning and constant pressure to get it all right were now all wasted. How she longed to see her sister again, to embrace as they last did, to talk of old times and to be together, just to be together again.

'Ma, I did the housework you tell me to do,' Shirley beamed with excitement as if she'd been handed a present. 'Look – I ironed all of our clothes and sweep the veranda for when Uncle Joe comes this evening.'

'Yes, chil, yes.'

'I even peel all the yam and sweet potato and green banana for Maureen to do.' The excited smile was turning into a disappointed expression, one that usually lingered on her face until she had been consoled. Her mother was tired, was always tired. She had to walk miles into town each day to sell bread and fruit. She sat and sold her food in the hot sunshine and then had to return to those long miles back home.

'But wait – where Maureen is, she ain't got here yet? Let she see something when she get here but look at me crosses nuh, I tell that girl to be home and have food done before I get in from town and she not here yet?'

It was usually bad when she talked like that, 'cause at first she didn't do anything then she'd wait and watch and see if you would do it again but even then she'd wait. The day that she caught you the third time, God help you, she would disappear and reappear with a long stick in her hand, you better not run 'cause it was then you'd get double blows and harder. Shirley recalled the day that her sister was found a little drunk in the cane fields; she was supposed to have gone down the line to Aunt Vi's house but met a boy she knew and sat drinking until her belly hurt and she fall asleep.

Although Ma licked her bad that night, you could see how much it upset her to do it. Maureen was Ma's favourite, even though Ma claimed not to have any favourites, that she saw each of her children the same. 'None was better than the other,' she exclaimed. Ma was always calling after Maureen, always wanting her to sit with her at night and rub down her tired legs with musterol. Somehow, no matter what Maureen did to her she still was the only person she called upon. It was all too often that Maureen was never around when she was needed. She'd be off down the line playing with the boys who whistled as they went past her house, to let her know that they were waiting for her. Maureen then checked that Ma was resting soundly out by the veranda before she could slip away. It wasn't until supper time that Ma would send me hollering for Maureen to get her tail in the house and cook dinner . . .

The family was quite a large one and Shirley was mainly responsible for looking after all her three brothers and Maureen's children as well. She practically brought them up while Ma was working hard to bring in the money to feed and clothe everyone. It was rare for the family to see their father around as they grew up, because he had run off with a young woman from town, then they both went to live in America . . .

As children, we hardly saw much of Ma. Sometimes she'd be gone for so long, especially when money was scarce, then she would be gone till really late. I used to snuggle down beside Ma's bed and prepare for my long wait for her to return but often I'd wake up to find Ma lying in bed and me lying beside her. Usually Ma got angry with me for burning the bulb for so long and wasting the electricity, which was one of the reasons why she had to go work for so long in the first place. So I soon stopped that and sat up waiting for her in the dark instead . . .

Shirley lay huddled on the edge of the bed, her hands were cold but sweaty, her legs felt numb and lifeless. Tears had escaped and found their way down the small strong face when she remembered the time that she received a letter saying that her mother had died. 'I was even the last to know,' she cried to herself.

Memories came rushing back of the shooting of her husband; the thought of not getting to see Maureen again, how long it would be before she got to see her kids once more, the fact that they probably didn't know where she was, troubled her all night. She longed for peace of mind, for the thoughts to stop bombarding her mind with question after question. Shirley rose from her bed, her arms and legs ached as if she had been engaged in a physical struggle of some kind. Her mind no longer seemed to whirl around, it was as if someone had taken her mind away and was saying, 'Yes, you've had enough troubles in this life.'

Slowly Shirley put her hand to her head and felt the small face, the nose, her lips, and gently she caressed her hair, her hair – how thin it had become, how coarse and very brittle. Hands thin and boney began to tug at her hair, it tugged at her clean white clothing, tugging constantly, angrily, bitterly. Shirley's small frame fell to the floor, lifeless, no cry was made to indicate the hardness of her fall, only soft whimpers were heard, silent gentle moans. Hands banged the floor, banged the walls, banged the doors for some acknowledgement of her existence. No one came. No footstep was heard from outside the door. Silence had unwelcomely invited itself again. Silence, silence louder than loud, the same silence which witnessed the murder that she had committed that long hot summer's day in July . . .

'You bitch, you, I only married you 'cause you was pregnant, you think I did care for you?' Shirley's heart now beating fast, she ran for the kitchen drawer and pulled from it a small black handgun. Her hands sweatingly pulled back the trigger. 'Oh, so you pull gun pon me now?'

Shirley realized that the time she'd been waiting for had finally arrived. 'I gone kill you, you bastard. You rape me chil, and tell me you marry me 'cause I was pregnant. You didn't know I know ain't it?' His face had turned now and was glaring straight into her face as if to say, how dare you acknowledge that fact to me. 'You tell me you'd hurt me and I wouldn't even know, well the table turn. You was jealous of us, why I don't know. I tried to make you like her and treat her like she was your own daughter but you had to take her from me. Why, why did you do it?' He held out his hand, pleading to her to put the gun down, but Shirley continued, she needed to get all her years of suppressed anger out and let him know what he'd done to her.

Tears rolled down Shirley's face as the words 'I only married you 'cause you was pregnant' played over and over in her mind. Everything I did and all those I loved you destroyed, you always kept me down, even when I fought to get our home set up, you refused to give me the money.

'Why did you do it to her, my baby, how could you do it, you fit to rot in hell. Your Ma think you so sweet, let she know what you did to Evenlyn, see what she'd say then.' Clenched fists tightened while his face and his hands suddenly came thudding down onto her, pulling her forward, allowing the trigger to go off, to explode itself right in his chest. He came down heavily onto the cold hard floor. Dead.

A little door to Shirley's room opened and in walked two nurses, neither smiled a hello, neither of them was Marica, where was Marica? They rolled up the sleeves of Shirley's gown and allowed the tiny needle to penetrate into her skin. Directed to the tablet and water, Shirley swallowed hard. Where was Marica, she hasn't come to see me for weeks, Shirley thought and quickly wiped the tear that was forming in the corner of her eye. The door was closed again and Shirley was left alone in that terrifying silence . . .

The knocking at the door made Shirley's heart skip a beat. She froze in her seat, then realized where she was. The cup of tea she held in her hand was cold now. The door was knocked again, this time louder, and voices could be heard from behind. Shirley straightened herself and went towards the door. Her body ached all over and she was feeling cold. Going past the passage window she noticed it was dark outside. 'What the hell is the time?' she whispered, annoyed with her casualness.

When the door opened there stood the loves of her life. 'Hello, Mum,' cried Evenlyn and pushed past the others to hug her darling mother. They were all there, her son, her other two daughters and Maureen.

'Well, don't look so shocked, girl, you tell me it was my turn to come down,' Maureen smiled and hugged her sister so tightly.

'Wait, sis, don't choke me to death now, you know,' cried Shirley, letting them into the house. The rest surrounded her with kisses and hugs.

A few days after the Black woman was found hanging in her room, Shirley was called to see her psychiatrist, who told her that doctors had agreed that her situation had improved and that she was to be allowed home within a few months.

Already the house seemed to have come back to life. Sounds of laughter and chatter could be heard in the kitchen now.

They all sat around the table which was laid with Shirley's finest tableware she used only for special occasions.

'I can't believe it, it feels like Christmas today.' Shirley grabbed on to her son's hand. 'Boy, you tall like ya father.' There was a short pause.

'Well, Shirley, it look like I'm going to be here for good, so you gonna be seeing plenty more of me and Tafferi.' Maureen held up her glass and toasted it to them all.

Shirley was filled with so much happiness she lost her appetite to eat.

'Es, what kind of hair style is that, it looks like you locksing.'

'Oh, Mum, I need to unpick it that's all,' said Esther uncomfortably, poking at her hair.

The atmosphere was high, the lights on in the house made it seem lived-in with the smell of roast chicken and rice.

'Mum, I wanted to tell you that you're a grandmother now,' began Carol, the second eldest daughter. 'I have a baby son.'

'Oh, Lord, what a blessing. Sweet Jesus, I thank you for keeping me alive and strong that I may continue living the rest of my life with my family whom I love dearly.' Shirley held out her hands to them, while tears rolled down her face. This time it wasn't tears of sadness but tears of joy and happiness, at last.

ZHANA

Apartheid Britain 1985 (Or Kenwood Ladies' Pond)

This pond is for ladies,
    so they say.
We don't have nannies to look after our babies
So I guess we should stay away.

A carpet of white bodies
Covers the lawn.
Why should we want to come here?
We don't need any sun.
We're already brown enough.
And it's not much fun
    when the ladies decide to get tough.

The water's beautiful,
But if we were to use it,
We'd only pollute it,
    so they say.
After all, dogs are dirty,
So are our husbands,
And so are we.

I'm surprised 100 trendy white girls
Can stand the smells
    our two bodies give off.
Our white co-workers
Know we don't *have* husbands,
But they lie still and say nothing,
Part of the carpet.

'Apartheid Britain' refers to an incident that occurred at Hampstead Women's Pond (otherwise known as Kenwood Ladies' Pond), in a posh area of North London, in the spring of 1985. Two Black women chose one of that summer's few beautiful days to visit the pond. Their ears were assaulted with comments such as, 'it smells here', and 'first their dogs, then their husbands'. After an argument with some of the white women, in which the lifeguard was totally unsupportive, they decided to leave. At that point, the lifeguard said to one of the white women, 'Well done, Linda,' and turned a handspring. The Black women then decided to stay for the remainder of the afternoon, regardless of the fact that they were subjected to continued abuse. Some of the white women present were trendy feminists, well known on the scene, and acquainted with the two sisters, but they did nothing to intervene.

A few months later, we staged a one-day occupation of the pond, to show that racists cannot get rid of us that easily. The weather was with us.

TOD PERKINS
The Decision

The nurse was welcoming. She didn't make me feel guilty, in fact was sympathetic. She stayed and chatted for a while, told me about herself and her mother. Her mother had been forty years old when she had given birth to her. I can't even remember how the conversation started as she was doing the usual pre-operational checks. Perhaps I was lucky, often people on the termination ward feel the staff unsympathetic, brusque.

Why did she confide in me? Surely she wasn't just making me feel comfortable? Two women sharing. Perhaps she was saying something she had felt the need to say for a long time. She loved her mother, wouldn't change her, but her mother had been forty when she had given birth. 'Forty-year-old mothers aren't the same as mothers half that age,' she had said to me, but she didn't elaborate.

I don't know her name, she wasn't on duty when I returned to consciousness. But I hope talking to me was of some benefit to her.

As I lay waiting for the ride to the theatre I knew I was doing the right thing.

There had been no inner conflict.

From the time that I had realized that the full and tender breasts were not just pre-menstrual, I had known that this child would never be.

For over twenty years my life had been geared to the wants of others. Now, with a new career and the children making their own lives, there was no way I wanted another baby.

Three children.

Three survivors, if you like – a son and two daughters. Perhaps I should have called them, withdrawal, durex and dutch cap.

I've been married nearly twenty-two years.

Is it really that long?

I've brought up a family almost singlehanded.

Well, he always provided, but I was the mother. He was there in between darts and cards and good friends. A real Jamaican father, so I have been told. Turning into the heavy Victorian moralist as the children became more independent.

Anything that went wrong was my fault.

One daughter getting pregnant at sixteen.

One running away from home.

Do I really want to go through all that again?

Perhaps late babies are hereditary in my family.

My mother bore my youngest brother when she was forty-two.

Lynda, my eldest sister, had her last child at the age of forty.

Hereditary.

For years I had been careful, taken precautions. Then my body dictated a need for change and even so it wouldn't give up the coil that had clung so tenaciously to my inside. I had had to spend a day in hospital and have a general anaesthetic in order to set right a minor problem that was causing trouble. So I reverted to the cap again. But like the disciples I had little faith, and within eighteen months I was pregnant.

How was it I made a decision to use a cap again?

I had no faith in it. I was embarking on a career, my family was grown, I was a grandmother.

I did not want any more babies.

Yet I could not make the decision to be sterilized.

My husband said I was too young to be sterilized. Too young! Even the medical profession regarded women of my age as too old to give birth without complications. He was hardly aware of what I was doing, his routine was not upset, life went on. Mine included studying for O-levels, getting a college place and working damned hard for a degree.

How much control do women really have over their lives, over contraception? Twenty years ago it was not free. Advice and help had to be sought, contraception was not a public matter. I had my three children close together, not by choice.

Would things have been different had I been given a choice? Would my life have been different if the children had been carefully planned and spaced out?

I love my children.

I loved my children, the pleasure they gave as little ones far outweighs the traumas and conflicts small children and their parents have.

I love my children.

The pain of their birthing soon passed.

The pain of their breaking away will always be with me.

It was not the way I wanted it to be. Could I have made it any different? I know that I do not want to pass that way again with another child. I don't want a second chance. Children do not choose us as parents. They are not our property.

> Your children are not your children.
> They are the sons and daughters of life's longing for itself.
> They come through you not from you,
> And though they are with you yet they belong not to you . . .
>
> Kalil Gibran

And so I made the initial decision on my own.

I had not expected my doctor to be so sympathetic. He was not the easiest of people to talk to. But, surprise, when the second test came back positive he wasted no time in referring me to the hospital.

As for my husband, the father, what was his reaction?

'Do we want another baby?' he asked when I told him I was pregnant. Leaving the final choice to me as usual, he concluded, 'Whatever you do, it's up to you.'

For most of the past twenty years I seemed to have had the final word. Not that I chose to have it but because he always said: it's up to you. So I forced a decision from him by asking the hospital authorities for a consent form, so that he would have to sign for the termination of his child that I had just conceived. He has not mentioned it since, and knowing him the way I do, there is not a way of ever getting him to discuss his feelings.

Thus the decision was reached. I did not consult my children. The girls were living their own lives and my son never stayed still long enough to discuss anything with him.

Once I asked myself, if they were still at home sharing a family life with us, would I have gone through with the pregnancy? Would I have been influenced by their views? I wouldn't have expected them as teenagers to share the childcare, but would have expected their support in other ways around the home and perhaps the occasional babysitting. The child would have been mine not theirs. Only my life would have been affected. What right would I have had to ask them to change to accommodate a younger brother or sister? I didn't ask them.

My elder daughter found out purely by chance once my bed and admission date had been confirmed. Watching a television programme where the same sort of situation had arisen and each family member's reaction had been different, she had said, 'It's none of their business is it, Mum? Would you let any of us influence you that way?'

'Well, it's too late for that – I am pregnant and I am having an abortion on Friday.' My statement hadn't meant to come out that way but I felt she understood by her reaction. 'Are you? Does Dad know? Do you want me to do anything?' Just a loving response. No recriminations or accusations.

I had felt tired for a long time, but apart from the absence of my period and the tenderness of my breasts there were no other outward signs of pregnancy and I looked forward to Friday with relief.

What a time to need an abortion. Final examinations under way, and I was determined to take them. After all those years of studying I could not miss them now. I was to sit the final examination and go into hospital the next morning. Final, finish, end of.

Because of the need to talk to someone on the college staff just in case my exams went badly, or I was ill or too exhausted, I chose to talk to the one tutor I felt would be approachable. How strange that the woman I chose to confide in had just gone through the same experience. She was supportive and understanding, telling me her own reason for having an abortion and subsequently being sterilized. Her reason was much the same as mine. She understood my tiredness and said that if I failed my examinations she would intercede for me; but she added that I would pass and had nothing to worry about.

As I lay on the trolley awaiting the porters who would wheel me to the theatre, I wondered briefly what I would do if I felt any movement within.

There wasn't and I had no need for heartsearching.

No one asked me in the anaesthetic room if I wanted to change my mind. I was surprised.

'Count backwards.'

I awoke to the sound of someone sobbing. The girl in the bed opposite to me was breaking her heart. No one approached her, in fact we all seemed to studiously ignore her, including the nurse who was now on duty.

Not the same young sympathetic girl who had checked me in. I am sure she would have found time to offer consolation to the distressed young woman who seemed to be regretting her move.

It was strange that none of us spoke to each other during our brief sojourn through that experience. None of us commiserated, commented or consoled each other. I don't recall looking anyone in the eye, smiling at anyone or nodding my head. We were as anonymous to each other as the child I did not want to bear. Perhaps that was the way it should have been.

All I wanted now was to know that I had passed my examinations and would be able to take up my position in September. Leaving the ward was like leaving a stage in my life. The future was all mine.

Since the abortion I haven't spoken much about my experience with anyone except people who have travelled the same road.

We all came to our decisions ourselves and I know mine was the right one.

ZINDIKA S. MACHEOL

The Real Sisterhood

As a girl I grew up surrounded by a large group of other girls, all of whom were my friends and similar in their background of being black and of having the immigrant experience. But they were also very different girls, with their own peculiar and effervescent personalities, and I believed they showed me the true richness of friendship. Within this group everyone had someone special – a best friend. This was always the person whom you sat next to on the bus or held hands with while walking down narrow or crowded streets; and of course, the person to whom you told all your secrets. My friend and I, we used to whisper to each other at quiet moments, walking arm in arm and giggling at some puerile secret . . . 'You're my best friend and we will always be best friends.' I was totally convinced that this was the way it would always be and nothing or no one could ever come between us. Ironically, we no longer see each other.

My life still revolves mainly around women: women whom I know well and not so well, a few good friends, acquaintances, and even women I could assume to be close to in sisterhood; all of whom have added their own strength, support and vision to the quality of my life. However, the term 'best friend' and all the perfect sentiments that it conjures up for me I rarely apply to any of the women I know and love today. Yet, I know I value their friendship as any other; but what my best friend and I had was something special. Ours was an organic friendship, developing without much contrivance from us. I remember we used to try and dress alike, walk and talk the same and style our hair the same. People used to ask us if we were sisters, even twins, and my friend and I would smile mischievously, as if to say, people are really stupid to think us twins or sisters; but at the same time we were pleased with their gullibility. More important than dressing up was communication. We would talk for hours about feelings, desires and frustrations. I think we found the same things in life similarly frustrating. I loathe authority and my friend did too. Racism incited anger in us, but what could we do? We were hapless victims caught in its path. At such times I found safety and retreat in our friendship and in the openness and intimacy with which we shared and expressed ourselves to each other. We were even blunt and critical at times but this was done out of concern and with the confidence of knowing that we knew each other well, rather than any wish to judge or contradict.

Summer was the best time for us. We spent a lot of time in each other's company, engrossed in the delightful world we had created for ourselves – inventing boyfriends and stage-plays in which we both appeared. Nothing else seemed important at such times except our devotion to each other. Sometimes the relationship was threatened if either of us found a new friend. Perhaps that was why we felt the need to keep on reinforcing the fact that we were best friends and this was reassurance for me. I became disappointed if my friend was ever missing from the crowd of girls we hung around with. What could I do? It was an irrational feeling; sometimes I was with a group of girls who were the most generous, humorous and affectionate people I knew – but I couldn't help feeling that my happiness or enjoyment was incomplete without my best friend on such occasions. Her cherubic face and smile is what comes to mind back in those lazy summer days of hotpants, funfair rides and the times we spent lying on our backs in the park and looking up at a clear blue sky.

In those days we were said to be typical of young Black women – defiant and aggressive – perhaps we were. I knew there was definitely a kind of fire burning in our throats – an undefinable fire which we could only express in our raucous and extroverted behaviour. We attracted much warranted attention and we revelled in our loud image. We were not afraid to speak our minds, neither did we care to act like nice young ladies as some said we should. In those days of childish antics and carefree dreams, we never gave a thought to the future or where we would be in it.

Around age seventeen, our friendship began to fade to the point where we didn't see each other any more. There was no dramatic point to this drift, and nothing was said between us about what was taking place. This was a bleak period for me anyway – for not only were my friend and I seeing less and less of each other but I was agonizing over the decision of what to do on leaving school. I could go into further education or get a job. However, with fermenting racism in society and the lack of opportunities existing for young Black people I didn't entertain the idea of getting a job for very long.

Failing all, I could roam the street in 'bad gal' style, chase boys and get pregnant. This was one of my biggest fears, the thought of being spermed by a handsome suitor whom I had met at some party or in the heat of some frenzied night-club beat. The initial contact with the opposite sex I found mildly pleasing – I kidded myself that I was actually going to enjoy the ritual of being chased. However, in the mêlée of finding myself a boyfriend was the pressing fact that he would have only one thing on his mind – sex. I developed a fear of pregnancy. 'If you get pregnant, don't bother to come home,' my mother used to warn me, and I was positive she meant it. I had visions of myself being cast out onto the streets or ending up in a hostel for bad girls or even a mother-and-baby home. This, more than anything, preoccupied my mind, especially when I heard of girls I knew to whom this had happened. So the result of my mother's fear and my own had a marked effect upon me. I began to associate men with pregnancy and pregnancy with vulnerability and rejection.

Around this time it seemed that all my friends with a sudden spurt began throwing themselves into the wonderful world of babymaking with its fairytale promises of love, marriage and monogamous heterosexuality – which was never really forthcoming either for them or for me. This sudden desire for men and motherhood perplexed me, and although I never really voiced any outright objections to their behaviour it did all seem to me to be quite shortsighted. It alarmed me when I saw them rushing into relationships which both they and I knew would be short-lived. Furthermore, it would leave them burdened with children which they neither planned or wanted. This, then, must have been the vague beginnings of our slow drift apart.

My friend was spending more time with her boyfriend and the time we spent together didn't seem so precious to her any more, whereas it still was to me. It seemed that we had reached that magical age when men were supposed to take priority in our lives. My friend had made the crossover and I hadn't. For this I felt myself being pushed out and almost discarded. The thought of being dislodged from the circle of friends whom I loved and trusted, frightened and troubled me intensely – what if I never made new friends, was the most worrying consequence I could think about. On the other hand, I was becoming irritable with them and their talk of men, babies and the constant competition to look good; all of which was increasingly isolating me from the crowd, and not least my best friend. Above all, I was adamant that I would not be put in a position where I would be judged by my biological ability or my attractiveness towards the opposite sex. So I sought my escape from this purdah of happiness; discarded my platform shoes, heels and pencil skirt, which I always thought were uncomfortable anyway.

Before long, my departure from my friends was complete. Shortly, I found my reprieve in education, travel and sisterhood, all of which embellished my life for a long time. The arrival of sisterhood signalled a point of discovery in my search for new ideals, and new groups of women who were conscious and determined not to fit any kinds of oppressive roles that had been designed for them. I joined a Black women's group and attended conferences where I was able to delve into the many facets of Black women's lives through consciousness raising. With this came the revelation that we could create our own arena of both personal and collective strength. I was captivated. In my feminist politicization I was assured of my independence and made aware of the many chasms which separated us from black men, white women and even the working-class, and to which the only solution was black women's autonomy.

In sisterhood I found my little niche, but this knowledge made me critical. Whereas before I had viewed my friends' activities sceptically, that scepticism now turned to bitter negativity. I thought them perhaps a little misguided and weak in succumbing so easily to male sexual pressures. I accused them of not being in total control of their bodies, and the way they constantly sought male approval of them baffled me – and (oh, yes), they did lack ambition. I had no time or sympathy for them any more. They made me angry – and why couldn't they be more like me? I saw myself as being enlightened whereas they were still in the dark. I hadn't seen them for a few years now and I'd heard that they were accusing me of breaking away from them. They blamed me and I blamed them, but never face to face. I wanted to see them again and share what I'd found with them, but at the same time I had total misgivings as to how they would view me. Plus there was the nagging factor that I had become too complacent in my independence and I just would not fit in anymore.

I saw my friend again the other day. We met by accident. She was pulling a shopping trolley behind her and looking harrassed. I was breezing along on my way to the women's centre. For a brief moment my friend and I hesitated before saying a shy and reticent hello. I wasn't sure whether it was because of our unexpected meeting, or just the fact that ten years had elapsed since we last saw each other, that made us act so like strangers towards each other. Anyway, I felt rather ridiculous at my reservedness, for it wasn't as if she was just any woman or just any friend. I was in fact staring into the face of the woman who had been in my dreams for the many years that I had not seen her and had wanted to see her. She was like a moonstone in my memory, a shared experience and part of the woman I was today.

It seemed that we were thinking along similar lines, for then we both threw up our hands in unrestrained glee and hugged each other. We stood for a while chatting, and she poured out her troubles to me with ease. She told me of a life spent working all hours God sent just so she could bring up her daughter decently. I could see that the constant struggle for survival had taken its toll in her weary mind and body – but what really struck me was how accepting she seemed to be of it all.

As my friend muttered her regrets, it seemed that the years of non-communication had slipped away with my voice and all that remained was a stubborn silence. However, I did recognize a familiarity in her plight and the fact that she wasn't just reflecting her own individual misery. To me what she was talking about was an overwhelming sense of powerlessness to control her life and her situation. Wasn't this what I had spent all this time in Black women's groups talking about?

I wanted to say to her, 'Look, sister, you're not in this alone. It's a universal struggle. Why not come along with me to the women's centre I'm on my way to?' It was on the verge of my lips but I didn't say it. Why? Because I could see that we were not the same people any more. Unlike in our teenage days, our outlook on life was different now. She now in her skirts and heels and me in my trainers and jeans. She with her hair in wetlook and me with my natural. She still spoke broad Jamaican, whereas I had perfected my English to its well-enunciated tones. So I was wondering where my friend would fit into the neat label of sisterhood which I had adopted to replace her. How would the sisters receive her, and, more alarming, how would she receive them?

Finally we parted in the streets with me saying very little about myself for I was afraid of how she would judge me. However, we did promise to meet up again and we did some weeks later when I visited her flat. We spent the evening reminiscing, between which she complained that she would be on the night shift again, cleaning up after other people. I was attentive to her daughter; and for a whole evening we refreshed a memory – so much that I even began to fantasize the idea that we could be great friends again, sharing emotion and time with each other. Then, sitting over the rice and peas, I told her a little about myself, which I had refrained from doing so far. I told her about the feminism and the political marches. Then she yawned and looked at me with dismay out the corner of her eyes and said, 'You, a women's libber, I can't believe it. You're not the person I used to know – the person I knew wouldn't go on any marches. Shame.' Her rebuff brought a lump to my throat and I was sad, for I had wanted her to say, 'Tell me more. I am interested,' but she wasn't. Immediately I felt a kind of dejection and a great sense of loss. Her response had confirmed my long fear that she and I were no longer an important part of each other's lives. So there I was confronting the startling fact that my friends and sisterhood were at opposite ends of a remarkable spectrum, reflective of Black women's life and experience. I had travelled the spectrum and come to the conclusion that both were still a part of me and my life. Yet I could not integrate the two in my consciousness.

So I question sisterhood, which in my experience has always suffered from many schisms; one of which was that we tried to achieve unity by assuming that all Black women are alike and want the same things out of life. Yes, we have common experiences, struggles and even goals; but the fact remains that we are different – and achieving these things might require a little bit more understanding between ourselves. I had spent a lot of time in Black women's group and knew that something was not quite right. For a start, where were the ordinary Black women whose lives were supposed to be reflecting our experiences? And whom we the supposed elites in the women's movement were suppose to be liberating? Women like my friend. The fact was that if they did turn up we might not even recognize them. For we would be too busy assessing the way they were dressed, whether they had a perm or were wearing too much make-up. I had heard sisters reject women outright on these criteria. The usual remark was, 'Their politics aren't right' or 'They just don't look like feminists.' In other words, they weren't dressed in slacks or dungarees with a neat trim of the hair or healthy growing plaits. You know, that look which says, I'm not dressing to please anyone – when in fact there is an overt dress code to please other feminists.

I've realized that years of sisterhood have made me incapable of seeing other more feminine Black women as being independent or as worthy of independence as I was. At one time, I remembered, the company of too feminine women made me uncomfortable. I always thought they looked down on me because I wasn't as well groomed and dressed as they were; and because in their eyes, I wasn't making the most of what little attraction I possessed, and in no way was this feeling of mine illogical. Turning up at parties in well-worn jeans and T-shirts when everyone else was slinkily attired therefore became my forte; for it guaranteed me the hostile stares which would leave me swelling with pride that I had made the powerful feminist statement I'd intended. To me it seemed that what feminism was saying was that our liberation was not only from men but from overtly feminine women too.

I recall whilst at college walking on the opposite side of the corridor to this other Black woman. Always when we passed we held our heads high and looked the other way or straight ahead, as if afraid to look at each other. Her reason being, she thought I was a rampant feminist who was going to preach to her. My reason being, she was just another feminine woman whom I hadn't a lot in common with. Eventually we were introduced by another friend and were both extremely amazed to discover that not only did we hold the same views culturally and politically, but we both had a passion for the same food, music and books. Much later we admitted to having misjudged each other purely by appearance. Now it's a wonderful relief for me to have broken that mould and to rediscover ordinary women again. I now know women who make no concessions about heightening their feminine appearance and they are as acutely political, expressive and liberated as any feminist I know. Yet they don't talk in concepts of feminism nor profess sisterhood. It is their openness and warm acceptance of other Black women that tells me that they, more than anyone, have the feel for real sisterhood . . .

This is why I've come to the conclusion that in grasping for our identity and self-awareness through feminist sisterhood we had become pushy, with a prejudgemental tendency which alienates other Black women who don't look or think the same way as us. Myself, I'm guilty of this to the point where I was rejecting my own friend for fear that she would not fit these criteria. I could see that there was no room for a woman like her within the one-dimensional world of political sisterhood we had created for ourselves, a world whereby we could only relate to each other in a context which did not necessarily encompass all the varied patterns of our lives.

Nowadays I'm somewhat woeful and conscious of being a misfit – wishing that my friends were more like the sisters, and the sisters more like my friends. Still I search for that elusive combination. However, I'm glad to say that I've mellowed with the years, and now I think how foolish I must have been to have displayed that amount of arrogance towards my old friends. I now view their experience as being every bit as valuable as mine. They have children and I have sisterhood. In surviving sisterhood I've found that not all my needs and expectations could be met or reciprocated. I can't say that I'm not disillusioned with sisterhood. I can't say either that I've found true friendship – not like the ones I've lost. I now view it as somewhat of a gigantic fantasy with many promises and many flaws which when revealed leave me feeling rather insecure. Still, I cling to it even if at times it appears with polished superficiality and hard pushy reality.

So I continue to wonder, where does the real sisterhood lie? Perhaps it lies with my friends for they were real and down to earth. I'm not saying that everything was a 'bed of roses' between us – it wasn't. I remember those traumatic years of adolescent uncertainty when my friends and I use to bicker a lot and would not speak to each other for long periods. However, they still remain poignantly gelled in my mind. Why? Because they were an important part of me; a living and spiritual substance which I still consider to guide me. Occasionally I go on these long reminiscences and with succinct velocity my mind races back to those early days. What is it that I'm still yearning for? Is it that innocent fondness for female closeness; or just the infatuated splendour of an irretrievable past I miss?

As for sisterhood, the notion that the whole woman race could be united is wonderful but at the same time unreal and unworkable. I see this more and more everyday, where sisterhood appears to me like a competitive arena – those who are weak get pushed out, and those who remain fall into amoebic patterns of division along political, sexual, cultural and creative lines which some women find are better at meeting their needs.

For me, the trouble with trying to achieve sisterhood first is that it does not lead to real friendship; whereas I believe only through friendship can the real sisterhood be found. That is why the memories of my friends linger potently in my mind. There was a closeness and a bonding between us which I've never managed to find anywhere else. I will never forget it. To me, that was the real sisterhood, then.

*

ZHANA

Fair Trade

*

Policeman, please
Can you tell me
What is a Black woman's
Life worth?
Constable, please
Can you tell me
In pounds and pence
What's my life worth?
What's it like when
Big boots carry blue coats
Through my front door?
Cherry Groce can tell me.
Should she be glad
You didn't shoot her son?
Which is worth more,
Her son's life or her legs?
Want to trade?
What's the rate of exchange?
She'll never walk again –
Is she hurt a little
Or a lot?
Is she in pain
Or does she feel nothing?
Do you feel sad –
A touch of remorse –
A 'tragic mistake' –
Or do you feel anything?

Cynthia Jarrett can tell me –
What's her life worth?
How many sacks of potatoes
Will one body buy?
How long did it take her to die?
Did she suffer?
You don't care.
I'm a big, Black woman,
Sometimes called 'Cynthia'
After the goddess of the moon.
Will I someday be
An ex-Cynthia?
Will you crash into my home
Looking for my son?
Push me out of the way –
A big, Black woman –
Taking up too much space.
Will I lie dying
As you stand over me,
The doctors pronouncing my death
Due to 'poor diet'?
A 'tragic mistake'?
An utter waste.
My beauty, my creativity,
Lost to the world,
My life lost to me?
Lying cold and dead,
What's my life worth, Mr Copper?
What's my body worth?
How much will you pay
For my legs, my back,
My brain, my heart?
What's your life worth, Mr Copper?
Want to trade?

*

ZHANA

Miseducation

*

I can remember sitting in classrooms, around the ages of nine, ten, eleven, being told by my Black teachers, 'Columbus discovered America.'

'Surely, they must know better,' I would think. 'They must realize how ludicrous a statement that is – America was here long before the white man came,' but no trace of a smile played around their lips. Grown-ups can be really stupid. Or maybe (I hope) they were just playing it safe.

Now I look at the effects the British education system is having on young Black kids. They come to accept everything white as the norm, and the norm is defined as being good. Therefore any time something Black is mentioned, it must, by definition, have a negative connotation attached to it. One girl at the Saturday school where I teach, aged about fifteen, can't understand why 'everything we teach has to be about Black and white'. She is one of the brightest students in the school, but she feels that anything we try to teach her about African or Caribbean history and culture is 'turning her against white people'. When, for example, I asked the children to pretend they were interviewing an editor of a Black newspaper, they demanded to know, 'Why does it have to be a Black editor? Why can't it be a white one?' This is the kind of question one would expect from white children. This appalling situation is compounded by the attitudes of parents who feel it is a waste of time to teach their kids about anything relating to Black history – 'What's the point of looking backward? We need to know the way forward.' Yet Black people living in Britain or the United States in the 1980s cannot have a sense of where we are now and where we are going, unless we first understand where we have been, how we got to this place.

The pressure on immigrants to assimilate into the dominant culture is very strong, especially when living, as we are, in a society which considers any culture apart from the dominant one to be 'aberrant'. In my experience, this pressure is much stronger in Britain, ie London, than in the US, where established 400-year-old Black communities are accepted as more or less part of the scenery. I can understand the need which Black parents feel to have their children 'succeed' in the terms defined by the dominant white society, to achieve professional status, to have a measure of material security. After all, without this material security, it is all too easy for Black people to be crushed, destroyed by this system which was built on our backs but within which we have no power. But I feel that, as Black adults in the community, we must be ever conscious of the fact that the schools were not built for our or our children's needs. In fact, I seriously question whether schools are meant to serve any children's needs at all.

The primary function served by schools is to prepare children for their roles in society, ie as workers. As Selma James points out in her pamphlet, 'Sex, Race and Class', this even extends to conditioning children to the belief that they have one specific role in society – that of student – while adults are playing their defined roles of breadwinner, homemaker, consumer, etc. While children are in school, they are given the kind of education that suits the needs of their future employers – they are taught to respect authority and to respond to external discipline. They are *not* taught to explore, to use their natural creativity and initiative, to question, to make mistakes which they can learn from, to take chances. This is especially true in the case of girls, whose good behaviour is more highly valued and gets them better grades than that of small boys, who are allowed a certain amount of disruptive behaviour up until the age when they are expected to become more 'serious'. In fact, so-called education teaches children *not* to explore their potential, not to try to find things out for themselves, not to question, but just to do as they are told. Western educational systems gradually and deliberately deprive children of their natural instincts for creativity and initiative, since these are not desirable qualities for worker bees. By the time children enter my class, at the average age of twelve, they are past questioning what goes on around them. If I should ask them a question, they sit with blank expressions on their faces, expecting to be handed the answer on a silver platter and prepared to swallow any information which is given to them by an authoritative source.

Since the little information about Black people they do receive in schools is almost always negative, erroneous and/or irrelevant, and since they are not taught from an early age to question or challenge the lies which we are daily fed about ourselves and our past, it is little wonder that Black children grow up with such negative self-image. Low self-esteem is the most important ingredient when one is cooking up low achievement, or even criminal and anti-social behaviour.

There is nothing wrong with Black children receiving high marks on their exams and attending the finest universities. Our children have the potential for high achievement and they are entitled to the best education that this system has to offer. However, it should be on their own terms. Black children, educated to have a strong sense of responsibility and self-discipline, along with concern for and pride in themselves and their community, can accomplish whatever goals they set for themselves in the white man's educational system.

DEBJANI CHATTERJEE

Distance

I used to wake to hear the chirping birds,
But now I hear the sound of whirring tapes –
A tape-recorder feeds my longing ear.
It seems I don't belong here, neither there.
I fled one land and hoped to find another,
And stepped from history into the future.
Our progress leaps ahead: once in its grip,
There is no resting and no turning back.
Monotonous, the monstrous whirring must
Go on to make the world a smaller place –
Bring countries closer, but drive men apart.
They study other cultures, lens in hand,
Distorting narrow robot hearts and brains.
I fled one land and hoped to find another,
But ignorant which buttons must be pressed,
I was imprisoned in my time-machine.

Mapping the Terrain

*

As the Black Women's Newsletter proudly proclaimed, 'We Are Here'.

When we came, we didn't quite realize what we were getting into. So, we continue to try to make sense of it all. Forming our support networks and creating our art forms are just some of the various ways in which we continue to define this society and our role in it. Meanwhile, we look back over our shoulders, deciding whether to remain fixed, move on or return Home to Mother. Perhaps not yet fully aware that, wherever we stop, we begin to put down roots.

DEBJANI CHATTERJEE

Voice and Vision

I speak in many tongues, my friend –
Moulded by the Black experience.
Languages are my inheritance.
I move in many cultures, friend –
Of necessity I make them mine,
Lightly treading in so many worlds.
I dream the only dream, my friend –
The glory that Martin Luther dreamt,
Stretching from our past to our future.
I'll never accept rejection:
With brothers and sisters I belong.
Our few are many, we're proud and strong,
We know our right and we'll right our wrong.

ZHANA

Meiling Jin and Zhana in conversation

Meiling and I have worked together for quite some time, supporting each other in our writing and putting together the *Funky Black Women's Journal. Gifts from My Grandmother** is Meiling's first collection of poems. I conducted this interview in 1985.

MEILING: If anyone asks me what I am, I use shorthand, I say I'm Chinese, or – it depends who I'm talking to, you see – I say, I'm Chinese Guyanese. A, people don't know where Guyana is, they think it's in Africa somewhere. B, they don't understand why I speak English.

I've got different ways of speaking, I can tell you. My mother's got a very very strong Guyanese accent which she'll never lose, and when I talk to my mother, I speak in a very strong Guyanese accent. When I talk to my sister, I speak in a very sort of heavy Chinese accent. And if I'm talking on the phone, I've got my social-worker accent. I think we learn to adapt.

It's to do with what immigration does to you. You come to a foreign or a strange country. I find when I'm abroad, I'll go to France or something and for the first few days I speak with a pseudo-French accent. I find it very difficult to express myself, in English. And I'm always grappling for words. It's this sort of going through the barrier bit, the going across the border bit, that really goes back to my childhood, you know, coming to this country. The upheaval that it causes you and the different cultural things and the different expectations.

ZHANA: I love the poem 'Strangers in a Hostile Landscape'. It says so much. You get this feeling of you travelling, being

* Sheba Feminist Publisher, London, 1985.

transported back and forth. And you deal with terms like 'colonization' and 'independence'.

MEILING: You can use it in all these theoretical debates and you know what it means, but it's also what it means in my terms. It means that when I go to another country, I stumble, I can't depend on English. It doesn't matter which country I go to, I always feel like that, I can't express myself. That's why that poem switches from the macro to the micro.

There are different class things working in the Chinese community. Because we have not come from a main area of Chinese emigration, we haven't really fitted in anywhere. You don't come across many Chinese people from the Caribbean.

When I went to China, it was the most amazing experience for me, because it was the first time in my life, and I mean in my whole life, that I ever felt normal. You're just going on visuals now, because I'm very very Westernized, I was born in the Caribbean and I've lived in the West all my life. I have a very different background. But there's a sort of emotional link, to see that everybody looks like you. On one level, you get this tremendous feeling of belonging, even though you're overseas Chinese and you're dressed quite differently. Even just visually, you get this tremendous sort of thing. And that, for me, is not enough to live there permanently, but it's very very affirming.

ZHANA: I think that is so important. There's no possible way you can overestimate that. That's why I want my kids to go to Black countries and see other Black people, not just live in a country where everybody you see around is white. That's why media is so important as well. If all you see are white people, if the authority figures are white people, you begin to think of white as the norm, and you will always see yourself as an outsider.

MEILING: That's why I got a shock when I came back. I got a shock when I went over there, cultural shock or whatever, when you go to the so-called 'third world', you get that sort of shock. You come over here, you get an even worse shock. When I was on the train, I just wanted to crawl under my seat and die, I was surrounded by all white people. And the only thing that made me feel a little bit at home was actually there were a lot of Black people on the train. There was that slight mix, and I felt a bit better, but I just felt really horrible.

I'm not sure how deep that goes. There's a big contradiction there, because we are very Westernized.

ZHANA: Until recently, you identified yourself as Black. Why was that?

MEILING: I was trying to identify with a particular set of politics, which was the politics of the particular Black women I know and I've seen around on and off. You and I have had many many discussions, because . . . it's wanting to identify with a struggle which is the same as my own.

ZHANA: Why do you no longer call yourself Black?

MEILING: Because there were too many meetings in which people said, 'and all of this riff-raff who are calling themselves Black and jumping on the bandwagon,' referring to Asian people, and by that I mean all people from the Asian continent. That hurt, and then secondly it made me very angry. I think on the political level I would see myself as Black, but when you say things about culture, I do feel, just from my conversations with you, I do know what you're talking about, and I do agree that there are those differences.

Why I called myself Black in the first place was to do with identifying with a certain set of politics. It's not that my politics have changed. It's just that I'm trying to recognize what differences we do have. I don't really want that to be a source of our differences, or an argument between us, because I think we've got enough to be getting on with.

ZHANA: Why poetry?

MEILING: Black women actually find poetry easier because you can write it on a scrap of paper, or whatever.

ZHANA: I've always thought of poetry as being difficult, as being about metaphors, or something esoteric, over there somewhere.

MEILING: There is a very heavy English literature influence. I notice with my own poetry . . . It's still along those lines, whereas American poetry has a different flow to it.

ZHANA: Yeah, well, it would do. White American poetry is different to English poetry as well.

MEILING: There's something about the word, the voice. Storytelling – my father used to tell us stories every evening. We used to crowd round and he'd tell us stories about Tarzan or whatever. I come from a long tradition. I love telling stories and I love listening to them.

ZHANA: How does being a lesbian inform your poetry?

MEILING: It means that I write more about women, I'm women-oriented.

ZHANA: How did this book come to be written?

MEILING: It was a collection of poems that I sent to Sheba. It was stuff that I'd written, and I put them together, and they just seemed to follow together. By the time they wrote back to me, I was changing, again and again changing. And by the time they agreed that it was going to be published as a collection, I had changed again. So more poems came to it, and different, other things came to it. The introduction is totally different. The introduction had to be longer, so I wrote more about myself. It became more like a sort of journey, charting a journey. Your experiences and how you identify and what you discover about yourself. It's about making connections with your past and with other people and with other women.

We were tossing up millions of different titles. It was going to be called *Secret Woman*. Then there was this thing in the introduction, I was talking about coming over here from Guyana, my grandmother gave us each a gold bracelet, and that was a memory that we each would have from her. From that, we got the title. It's a gift that she's given us, as well as her experience that she's given us.

ZHANA: You have this ability to have one small sentence sum up a lot. One small concrete image, like punching someone's teeth out. Teethmarks on the bread from 'Rats', that's right there, you can see teethmarks. It's right in front of you.

MEILING: Yes, we used to have a lot of rats when I was a kid. You could see the teethmarks on the biscuits and we'd just take the little bits off. My mother insisted we not waste anything.

ZHANA: Where does the ship Red Riding Hood come from?

MEILING: The ship Red Riding Hood was the real name of a real ship that my grandfather's father jumped.
ZHANA: Why 'A long overdue poem to your eyes'?
MEILING: When I was a child, it was my eyes that always betrayed me. People used to come up to me and say, 'Your eyes are so funny. Does it hurt you? Is it painful for you to not have any eyelids?' I used to get that all the time at school. 'Can you cry?' and that sort of thing. And that's really really painful. The boys used to say, 'You're all right up to here,' and then they used to put their hands over my eyes. I remember sitting in a shop and a man came up to me and then he jumped back and said, 'Your eyes scared me for a minute.' He was having a joke. It's this thing that's always betraying you, it's making you visible. All the time you're walking around trying not to be visible. And that's your most vulnerable point.

I used to go to the Saturday morning cinema, and I used to get so much racism. I used to get there, when they were queueing up, I didn't used to stand in the queue, I used to go about five minutes afterwards when everybody was in. So you got in the cinema and it was all dark and that was all right. And I used to come out really early, before the film was finished, because I just couldn't stand the level of hatred. (This was over here.) Hatred and real animosity. I used to make up stories. If I got caught in the crowd coming out, the kids would say things like 'chinky' and all the rest of it. I used to make things up about my father being an airline pilot or something. You make up fantasies to try to deal with it.

Real levels of self-hate go very deep. If you're a kid and everyone's always saying, 'Your eyes scare me', or this that and the other, or 'chinky' or that, you do end up hating yourself whether you like it or not. And although you go through all your processes and your consciousness raising which tells you you're wonderful or just tells you to be, deep down there's something in there that still hurts. And there's something about yourself that you really do hate.

It's negative stuff that's coming at you anyway – you're dirty, chinky, yellow, whatever, you know, that sort of makes its dent somewhere along the line. There's that and also the total absence of any role models or anything, seeing derogatory pictures of Chinese people's laundries or whatever.

ZHANA: In the poem, 'The Journey', there's a line that says, 'a woman appeared to me in my dreams and told me to stop talking to death and get on with it.' There's a real sense of irony there.

MEILING: I felt that, I think, from the We Are Here conference. I could feel words coming out of my earholes practically. We're always talking about this magazine that we're going to set up or this that and the other, or about our differences yet again, and I just felt I wanted to get on with it.

ZHANA: Future plans: are you going to bring out a collection of children's stories?

MEILING: Not a collection. I'm very interested in children's picture books. There are not that many around for Black children. I do like writing for children. I do enjoy it, and I feel they are very worth writing for. I'm very interested in magic and imaginary landscapes and that sort of thing, and I think children have this ability to follow you wherever you go. I feel really at ease talking about these things. Plus, my politics inform my decision to write. I remember, as a child, not having any books with *me* in them. There were always these blond-haired white children. I really want to redress that balance. There's not that many with images of Black children in them, there's just not enough. You could write until you're dead and there'd still not be enough. What really brought it home to me was, at a Black women's conference, there were all Black children in the nursery, and I picked up a book by chance. It was about two white children, and I thought, my God, we're out here revolutionizing, and you come into the nursery and it's the same!

Librarians tell you, 'These are the universal children's books. All children love these books.' They're . . . all books with white children. If you argue with them, they tell you, 'This is what the children like.' One Black woman said, 'Of course it's what they like, if you're ramming it down their throats all the time.' But there's nothing else. Some people try to write anti-racist, anti-sexist children's books, but they tend to be very boring, unfortunately.

Increasingly, a few good ones are appearing – Grace Nichols has written *Wriggly*, and Buchi Emicheta has written *Titch the Cat* – but I haven't seen many picture books. I'd love to be able to draw.

ZHANA: There's still time, you can learn.

MEILING: Well, yeah, in the future.

*

LENNIE ST LUCE

The Mango and the Kiwi Fruit

*

my sister and I are like mango and kiwifruit
i am the mango
luscious, obvious and rich
with a taste that at first is wonderful
but too much,
taken all to easily
is way way too much.
My sister is a kiwifruit.
an intriguing outside
that can appear abrasive
but is much softer than it seems
a colour that can look much duller than it is
or sometimes evokes a second glance
is it mysterious green?
Or an interesting shade of a subtle brown?
The inside defies expectation
with a startling beautiful contrast of colour
a smooth texture with myriad pips –
an undulating taste with a definite nip
thrill on your taste buds
that tingles and tantalizes.
How do you get so much in such little sizes?
Mango and kiwi fruit could never be the same
but they discord and compliment
in a fun-to-play game
together I think the mixture is snappy,
the mango the kiwi
the Lennie the Caffy.

TOD PERKINS

Journey to the Caribbean

'Mind how you drive back home and please remember the neighbours. We still have to live next to them when we get back, so don't play your music too loud.' These were my final words to my son when he left us at Heathrow airport at the start of my journey to the Caribbean.

For many years, as our family was growing up, Dougie, my husband, had often asked me if I would like to visit his home. His home was Jamaica and we had once, during those twenty years, managed to save enough money for him to return.

Both his parents had been alive then and he had always wanted me to meet them. However this was not to be. His mother and father died within eighteen months of each other and in 1980 he returned alone to erect their tombstone. In the following four years our two daughters left home to become independent. I studied for a degree and obtained a job which boosted our finances, thus enabling us to save for my previously unobtainable visit. But more important than that, I had, during those years, discovered my eldest sister Lynda, alive and living with her very large family in Trinidad, my long-dead father's birthplace. So not only did I want to visit the 'Land of Wood and Water' discovered by Columbus – I had to go and renew my acquaintance with my sister and brother-in-law, John. Yes, I have to say acquaintance because, after our initial letters of discovery and introduction, Lynda and John wasted no time in coming to London to meet us.

When we began asking questions and writing letters, my younger sister, Isha, and I had hoped to discover information regarding our father who had died when I was six years old and Isha a babe of five months. Never did we dream that our family would be increased by over thirty relations when I was given an address in Trinidad to write to by a stranger who had heard my radio appeal.

So at last we went off to Jamaica, Dougie's birthplace, and Trinidad, home of my sister Lynda and her large family.

By the end of the first week, I'd written in my journal about the things I'd seen. In the Jamaican high summer, rain had not fallen for several weeks. Brown dust, brown people, young, old, all seemed to reflect the poverty that the dry dust exaggerated. This was contrasted with the wealth, the houses of the wealthy secluded on the mountainside, while below them, amongst the banana trees, willow, poinseannas and bamboo were tiny little hamlets.

I wrote of the hills, the higglers in the market, the mango and ackee trees. But how did I feel there, where Black people were in the majority and where I found myself listening to white people speaking, to hear if they were Jamaicans not Americans or English tourists? Why, I don't know.

The realization that Black people were in the majority did not strike me until, one afternoon as we drove into the city, we passed a building site. The site was a hive of activity with workmen all over it. The workmen were all Black.

Had I expected anything different? I hadn't thought about it before. A holiday in Jamaica, everyone was Black, that was obvious when we drove in from the airport. So why was I suddenly struck with this inexplicable awareness?

I don't know. I thought about it that week, but haven't found an explanation.

One day, we passed a roadside stall staffed by a Rastafarian. A small, strong community lives on the highway leading to Old Harbour, and they survive by selling charcoal and homemade implements. Someone told me how these small communities were establishing themselves in some parts of the island. They had squatted on the site for some years, gradually increasing the size of their shacks, building more permanent structures, announcing their identity by painting their homes with the now familiar colours, red, gold and green. They were self-supporting.

We passed evidence of this as we drove along the Bustamante Highway, as we travelled the roads of City Kingston. Charcoal, carvings, straw mats, hammocks. Rastafarian craftsmen, living their lives, supporting their families. Yet the most despised group of people on the island are the Rastas. No self-respecting Jamaican non-Rasta would admit to feeling anything except animosity towards these 'Ganja-smoking, long-haired idle Black men'. Who would give them jobs? I heard nothing said in their favour, just as in England, and who despised them the most? Their own people.

One day, we visited Morant Bay. Several Jamaicans that I met in England knew vaguely of the place and the name Bogle. Few could tell me of the uprising that took place in 1865, and the subsequent slaughter of rebels and the hanging of Paul Bogle who, with William Gordon, led several hundred local people to the Governer's house to protest about land allocation after the emancipation. Queen Victoria had exhorted her loyal subjects to be diligent and toil hard after they had petitioned her for a fairer share and a better deal. (This reminds me of another female in a position of power today.)

The local police, called the Custos, were besieged in the town centre when the uprising took place. Both sides suffered many casualties and eventually the English soldiers were used to search for and bring in those rebels who managed to flee. Bogle was hung. Today, his statue stands in National Heroes Park, a belated tribute to one who stood up for his rights and those of his brothers and sisters.

Jamaica is a beautiful island. Columbus was right when he called it 'Land of Wood and Water'. Or perhaps he just interpreted the Carib name for it. Whatever, despite the drought, the island is a beautiful place.

In Jamaica I saw people of every shade, working in all sorts of places and in varying positions. No longer was it the case of the lighter your skin, the better position you would hold. Banks, government offices and hotels all appeared to be giving equal opportunities. Unlike Trinidad, where I was to find things very different, skin was not the most important criterion.

But I feel so much sadness for the place as well. I feel sad for the lack of resources that could set this island financially back on its feet. I feel sad that investors should listen to noise of violence and disturbance and not have faith enough to try for themselves. I feel sad that politicians should use the people in the way they do.

Nowhere in Jamaica did I hear politics discussed by Jamaicans. By expatriates and visitors, but not by residents. Not all the violence in the city is by rudeboys and criminals. People are shot for their political views as well. Where do honest discussions take place?

I feel sad that the haves should have so little regard for the have-nots. That they blame all the unrest and the consequences on the 'idle and the poor them', while they sit behind their grilled verandas or holiday in Miami.

Oh, Jamaica, the world is not perfect, I know. But so much could be put right if the people could be united, if the politicians were for the people, if pigs could fly.

At last I was going to my father's birthplace, to see my sister Lynda and her husband. I had already met my sister Lynda eighteen months before, when, after we had discovered each other, she and her husband had flown to London to meet us.

Twenty years my senior, Lynda was already a mother when I was born and my father a grandparent, though I doubt my mother knew as she struggled to make a home for us in grey Birmingham, my birthplace.

Thus I was going to meet nieces and nephews, some of whom were older than me. Those who had written to me over the past two years had jokingly written 'Dear Auntie' at the beginning of their letters. But my youngest nephew was only two months younger than my eldest son. Lynda was later to remark, 'You see, we were doing the same things at the same time.'

I was looking forward to seeing Trinidad, to meeting some of my father's contemporaries and hearing about him. Perhaps I would meet some older relatives as well. I knew there was an aunt who had helped to rear Lynda. But how would I find these other members of my suddenly extended family? Lynda was totally John's wife, she did everything for him and he expected her to. Were her children the same? How would they take to me? A wife, but independent with my own views and not averse to saying so. Trinidadian friends in England had often said the most chauvinistic men in the world were the male Trinidadians.

How would I find Trinidad in comparison to Jamaica? I had already been comparing Jamaica to England and Southern Ireland. Where would Trinidad come in my views?

My friends in the UK who joined me once a fortnight at our Caribbean workshop would be interested in my comparisons. The workshop had been formed to provide a place where people could meet to talk about their heritage and culture and find ways of preserving it and sharing it with others. This journal is for them as well as being a lasting reminder of a very special trip.

A reunion, a holiday, a fact-finding mission?

Trinidadians, like Jamaicans, seem terrified of their own downtown areas. In London, there are areas where visitors are warned not to go out at night. There are areas where one is warned it is not safe to go at any time. A visitor from another planet would believe that every other person had been mugged, raped or worse, and that every young man was a potential violent criminal. People have terrible tales to tell, most of them second- or third-hand and richly embroidered. So it was, here in the Caribbean.

All the adults we met complained of the state of the country's finances. The oil boom was over, the spending was supposed to be at an end. Everyone was tightening their belts. The traffic on the road belied this. The lifestyle of the people we were meeting did not give credit to the complaints. In Port of Spain, the rush hour lasts all day. Since the oil boom, so many people have acquired cars. Very few old cars are to be seen, and even the older ones appear in excellent condition. The majority of the cars are Japanese. It is not uncommon for a household with several teenagers to possess several cars. No doubt the people we met worked hard and were thrifty in their own way, but they were not living as if the banks were about to call in their markers.

Norma, my niece, is several years older than me. We became

friends immediately. I felt as if she were a sister. She was married with three daughters and a fourteen-year-old son. Like me, she was also a grandmother. Her years of married life have not been too happy but she has fought back, saved her marriage and kept the family business going. We found there was so much we could talk about, we had so much in common. No, my marriage hasn't been like hers, but I felt we were from the same mould. Strong women if you like, definitely kindred spirits.

One day, we went out to the beach. She told me that it was a long time since the whole family had united on a beach trip. Having visitors from England was good for them.

This beach was where Lynda and her husband, John, had brought them every summer as young children to spend three weeks of their vacation. A house had been rented and they had played as children on the beach and watched the seines being hauled in. Yet they had never learned to swim.

Whenever they had ventured too far into the water, Lynda had cautioned them.

Lynda hadn't changed. She worried about all of us in the sea and about the grandchildren enjoying themselves. Constantly cautioning them. In fact, I put my foot in it by saying that she made them fearful and should let them be more adventurous. I had noticed how dependent even the teenagers were on their parents. Or were the parents just too dominating? Chatting later to a great-niece, one of Norma's daughters, she admitted that she felt tied to her mother and that perhaps she was not adventurous enough. Married with two young sons, she lived in a small apartment added on to the main family home. Mama was always close.

My sister Lynda married John when she was sixteen years old. Our father had been somewhere in England, and her mother was dead. Two aunts had helped to bring her up. She was probably lonely and in need of someone to cherish her. I know the aunts were not pleased that she had chosen someone much darker than her. He was also a 'dougla', part Indian. Within five years of marriage, Lynda had four babies, followed by a breakdown. She didn't reveal how long she was ill, but about four years later she had another child, quickly followed by three more. Jasmine and Sherwin are the youngest, born to her in late middle-age.

Lynda's whole life has been devoted to her husband, her children and the Catholic church. John expects and Lynda complies. Her older daughters remonstrate with her and constantly beg her to do less. They appealed to me to speak to her.

I did. But to no avail. Lynda says she cannot change after all these years. Her health is poor and she suffers constant backache, but, she says, what would John do? She also said that her involvement with the church was her respite from the family. What could I say to that?

It usually took a lot of persuading on my part to get Lynda to agree to a day out. When she did come, she was never ready when we should have been leaving to go out. She was always busy trying to complete a meal or a task while we were waiting. I know she felt guilty. When I offered to help or told her not to worry or bother, she was ready with an excuse.

One day, we went to visit two friends, Albert and Lucille. Lucille was still recovering from the effects of a terrible accident when she and some friends were leaving a funeral and were mown down by a runaway car. Several of the women were killed; Lucille sustained severe injuries and was almost killed. Albert had worked at the same school that my own father had worked at before he left Trinidad. This time, while the men drank, I stirred the pot by raising a discussion on the role of women in the home today, compared with the older Trinidadian woman. It appeared to me that the older woman was almost subservient to her husband, doing all for his benefit and pleasure, and supposedly gaining pleasure from it while working herself into the ground. I think the men were surprised at the stance I took, because they were all truly chauvinistic, except perhaps Albert who, since the accident, had become far more aware of how much Lucille did. They now helped each other.

While we were talking, Lucille disappeared, eventually emerging with trays of curried lobster, rice and salad. Totally unexpected and extremely delicious but rather proving my point.

I was aware that the men didn't really approve of my forthright speaking, and later Dougie told me that they probably couldn't believe that he let me get away with that sort of attitude. But I felt very protective towards Lynda. On one of the rare occasions that we persuaded her to come out with us, she kept thinking of excuses for not accompanying us. One was that she couldn't take the responsibility for looking after us and directing our day out. Dougie and I told her that, even if she didn't come, we would still go, and if she decided to come, we would look after her! Although Lynda is my sister, I feel more as if she is an aunt. Not only because of her age, but also because of her attitude towards herself. She regards herself as old.

I feel certain that the day out was the most restful Lynda had had since she knew we were coming to Trinidad. She was minded by us. She didn't have to think about or prepare food, nor did she have any great-grandchildren to worry about. She was able to relax completely, lazily swimming in the warm, refreshing water, lying dozing on the beach and chatting. I'm so glad she came. Not only for the pleasant time spent in the water, but also for the chance it gave me to talk to Norma again. We talked about Lynda and the way John and Sherwin exploited her. About sons in general and their relationship to their mothers. Perhaps I had made my children too independent. Ian was at home in England looking after himself. Sherwin, his Trinidadian cousin, was not averse to telling his mother off if he came home and she hadn't left a meal prepared! No, he wouldn't dream of getting anything for himself. Ian can sew, knit and cook; his cousin can't. We talked some more about ourselves and our own personal lives, our hopes and aspirations, Norma's wish to visit the UK. It was difficult to leave the warm sea.

I found my attitude towards time was very different to the Trinidadians'. The English in me found the attitude that 'any time is Trinidad time' very irritating. But once we finally got there, I loved the time we spent on the beach, playing in the sand, swimming in the Atlantic, enjoying freshly-caught seafood which we could actually watch being hauled in. My connections with the Caribbean workshop enabled me to sound quite knowledgeable when we discussed food.

I met some men who had known and worked with my father, but strangely, they were not able to tell me very much. They said nothing about his early life, and no one knew anything about his exploits in England. They admired him because he had gone to England and, they thought, to Africa (I have my doubts). He was supposed to have written books and articles, but no one had any. And the school where he had taught, and where one of the men had been the Head, had burnt down, so I couldn't even see the plaque that was supposed to have had his name on. What an enigma Ernest Nicholas McKenzie-Mavinga was. Trinidad revealed very little about him.

I saw a lot of Trinidad, but so much of it was rushed that I know I have to go back to see all the places I didn't see, and have a better look at the others.

Although the Trinidadians are beginning to feel the recession, they give the impression of still enjoying the good life. And why shouldn't they? The poverty of Jamaica is not reflected here. I like the country and the people, and I want to return. The scenery is beautiful, though not as dramatic as that of Jamaica. Both beautiful islands, in their own ways. One day, I'm going back to both places.

I wonder if my views of the two islands I have visited and the people I met would be different if the visits had been in reverse order. I found the Jamaicans more friendly, more sincere and less preoccupied with skin colour than the Trinidadians (leaving out my own family). This is an impression I got listening to other Trinidadians, reading the papers, and while visiting in general. During one visit, one of the men remarked to Dougie that he had shown the same sense as my father, having married a light-skinned woman. Did that mean that these septuagenarians looked for colour before affection and feeling? It certainly seemed so, and it appears to have continued until today.

In Jamaica I never heard anyone discussing politics. In Trinidad it came into every conversation. And the Prime Minister was to blame for everything. Calypsos are written about him, mainly derogatory. I heard many jokes of which he was the butt. I wonder how the poor man ever reached his position.

Trinidad may no longer be as rich as she was but she certainly is not in the same state as Jamaica. There are very rich families who own most of the country's wealth, predominantly Indian. There are the middle-classes and the new middle-classes who plead poverty but their lifestyle belies this. And of course there are the working-classes, the poor and the very poor.

Perhaps I sound as if I am biased towards Jamaica. I love both places and can regard both as a second home. I have blood ties in one country and Dougie's family live in the other. I have tried to be honest about my impressions and feelings on what was my first visit to the Caribbean. I want to go back. I would like to spend some time on each island without family, then join them after a week or so.

We were made welcome by all. Who would be upset if I made a decision to live on the other island? Well I haven't got to make that decision yet, if ever.

I am a Black person living in a white man's country, even though it is now declared to be multicultural. England is the country of my birth, my home. Where I end my days is another matter. I teach very young children. I try to teach them respect and tolerance for each other, to appreciate what each has to offer; they are the future of this country and may never have the chance to visit the home of their grandparents. On my visit I saw and met Black people in positions of responsibility. I myself have proved what we can achieve in spite of obstacles and bigotry. I have always known my worth and have done my best not to let circumstances deter me. Seeing this in the Caribbean makes me more determined that all the little ones in my charge see me as an example and get the best start they can possibly have.

I won't be the only person to benefit from my wonderful holiday.

*

YVETTE CORT
Oral History

*

Black person, Black woman, Black mother. Here I have stated the basis upon which I determine my principles and make my decisions while raising my sons as an investment in the future of all Black people.

YVETTE: There is an awful lot that interests me, I suppose, and I'm now nearly thirty-one and I find my life is extremely messy. It's not as ordered as I like. There are numerous things that I'm interested in that I don't have the time to pursue. Also, I'm constantly finding out about myself, as a woman, as a Black woman. I'm constantly trying to understand where I stop being just a woman and start being a Black woman. About the whole way my Blackness has been part, it's an integral part, of who I am. I can't separate the two. And I'm quite angry about that. Because I had no control over that. I can never just view things as Yvette. I have to be the Black Yvette and that is how society sees me. And I have to accept that. Just for my own sake, I have to recognize that and accept that and deal with that. But I've had no choice. Nobody asked me if I want that. It's what I was born into, it's my heritage.

I also feel, at this time of my life – I came to this country when I was three, with my parents from Guyana. As I said, I'm now thirty-one, so I've been here all of my life. I've never been back to Guyana. And I sometimes have to ask myself, what am I doing here with my children? I have three sons. I am pleased my parents came when they did. I think I've gained an awful lot. And I think after living in this country I can live absolutely anywhere in the world and cope. But I still find myself asking, what am I doing to my children? Why am I staying here? Why am I putting them through this? I don't find it an awful lot of work bringing them up because I have terrific family support. We all live very very close. I don't have aunts and uncles here but I have immediate family, four brothers and sisters and Mum and Dad. I don't keep many friends, Black or white. I mean, that's just me. That is me, Yvette. I'm a little bit of a loner, I think, I tend to do as I see fit without consulting people.

I have a great fear of staying in this country with my kids. I don't intend to die here. I'm not sure where I'll go. 'Cause I think I am stateless. I don't particularly want to go back to Guyana. I have this dream of settling in Kenya one day. Whether it will come to fruition or whether it's unrealistic or whether the culture shock will be too much I don't know. But I'd like to give it a try and if I fail, I fail. If I come running back after a few years, so be it. But it will always be there.

I'd like to settle in an African country. I want to live in a country where Black people rule and Black people sweep the streets and Black people are commonplace. After growing up in this country all my life and seeing white people in all those positions of power, it took a few years before, as a Black child, I even realized that Black people had the sort of brains to do these things. I really wish my own children had the opportunity to see that themselves. My parents fed me lots of magazines and things from abroad, so I was fortunate, but a whole heap of my friends didn't have that. My parents were terribly aware of what was lacking in this country.

Education

YVETTE: I realized I was lucky. I was very lucky. My parents were both very intelligent people. My father was a policeman in Guyana and my mother was a teacher. When they came here, of course, they didn't enter either of those professions, they worked in the canteen or something somewhere. They had different jobs. And these were two very bright people. But the fact that they didn't carry out work with any particular status didn't mean that they allowed that to get them down. They were both optimistic people and they wanted good for their children and I thank God I had the parents I had. Because of my schooling here. I mean, I never had any problems with teachers, no direct problems because one visit to the school by my father or mother would make them realize that, if they wanted to take issues on board, then they'd better think twice because this person was not going to allow them to walk all over them. And I remember my sister and myself being two of the few Black kids in school who didn't attend ESN classes. My father would have absolutely gone berserk if any of the teachers had suggested that we were educationally sub-normal 'cause we jolly well weren't! But a lot of my friends weren't educationally sub-normal. Because they had come a little bit older than me, they had spent maybe the first eight years in their native country, and the words were slightly different. The teachers would say they couldn't understand what they were saying and they were stuck into classes for educationally sub-normal children.

ZHANA: The teachers couldn't understand *them*.

YVETTE: That's right, so the children were penalized. And, of course, that stigma stuck with them throughout their schooling. And a lot of their parents didn't feel able – they'd just come to this country, they couldn't take on the system. One they weren't aware, and two they didn't have the sorts of information that one needs to have to really take on the system. It's jolly hard.

In Guyana and other parts of the Caribbean, the only white people you saw were affluent white people. They were all terribly prosperous. You were told that the streets were paved with gold, you were told that the white man knew best. I don't know where my father got his bolshiness from, but he's never been able to accept that and I, really, to this day, I still don't know where, how come he was able to challenge it even in Guyana and couldn't take all that on board here. He never allowed us to think that white people were better or *anything* like that.

There were numerous things that happened to me in my childhood that I didn't fully understand. I remember the fact that my parents poured so much in, into me – to think about my identity, to be proud of what I am, to do well, to achieve – from a very very early age, but it wasn't a question of whether you achieved or not, it was *you achieved*. It was never a question that you didn't do well at your schoolwork. And I grew up with this very blind sort of attitude that, if books were there, you studied, you achieved, and I didn't know any different. When I look back, we lived in terrifically poor, slum accommodation and yet I had all these middle-class (so-called) values all around me all the time. None of that was taken into consideration by teachers, I was a poor Black kid from the area and that was it.

When I think of the way some of my white friends at school lived, I mean, we would *never* have been allowed to conduct ourselves the way they did, we were all very mature for our age, we could be taken *anywhere* really. And, um, the whole thing about behaviour, about the way you spoke to adults, all those sorts of things, I felt quite old quite early. I was still a child and I didn't have any worries to think about, my parents did. There was food on the table, we were always dressed and everything like that. But there were always comments about me and my brothers and sisters being so polite, so well-behaved, so intelligent, so this, so that, but it was nothing more than my parents expected. They didn't expect any less.

Because I've grown up with that attitude to my elders, I still feel it. To be honest, I feel it even with white people, that if they're older they have lived longer than me. I might have umpteen degrees or whatever. But they have lived longer than me. They have experience of living on this earth longer than me. So they always know that little bit more than me and I have to respect that. And that's Black or white and I would hope that my children, well, I think they have picked up the same thing as well. I do think that when it comes to education, particularly in the early sixties when a lot of us moved here – a lot of Black families, even the poorest Black families, who came from very poor conditions in the Caribbean – when it came to education they held very middle-class values. Because they maybe couldn't read or write very well, or they didn't have the opportunity because a lot of the time after primary age you had to pay and a lot of families didn't have the money – didn't mean that they didn't want their children to achieve and I think that's what the teachers misunderstood. Because the equivalent white child's parents didn't have much and didn't particularly care, that didn't mean that that immediately was the attitude of Black people who had come here to try and make something of their life. They came here to take it all on board.

You talk about your parents or other people going over the top about a piece of paper, I hear myself. To me the most important thing – nobody can take it away from you – your education, once it's there, it just changes your whole outlook about everything. It doesn't matter if you're sweeping the streets. Once you've got it, nobody can take it from you. That is what is important. It does influence everything you do in your life. Getting a piece of paper is important too, I feel, but the main thing is that you have the opportunities presented. You may not get the piece of paper, so what? It's the process you go through during that time that is of terrific importance.

It improves your mind, but the other thing is that, yes, education is one thing, but to me, you may get your piece of paper and not get a job but it's the confidence that it gives you to maybe think about steering into another direction, about the way it makes you value yourself. Because you realize that you have things that you enjoy, you can do things for yourself, you are somebody. I mean – that's what education does. I can hold my own no matter where I am and that is of terrific importance for me as an individual. 'Cause I know it makes me feel very good about myself and that is of primary importance.

To put it on a very basic level, I've lived on a very working-class estate for many years. I was just another young mum except that I was Black. And, um, little things like in the summer holidays, money was short, I wasn't working, those were the very early years with the kids. And so I went to the library, the library's free. I got the leaflet, I spread it out on the table, and saw they have different plays and shows in the parks. They've got a city farm. All these things that are educational for my kids.

Because they're city kids, they can go to the farm, learn about the animals, feed the chickens, and milk the cows. All it cost was a bus ride, about 20 pence a way. Got the kids dressed today and then all their other friends wanted to come as well. I mean, their mothers hadn't even thought. It's not around money, it's about being able to know where to go to find out information. Things like that, so when you don't have the money, you can still provide things for your children. I can pick out numerous examples. They have plays on sometimes. Some of the kids had never been to theatres and that. It is expensive, but if you go to the early matinee, it's 50p per child. And you can actually find a lot of bargains, and you've got to think like that. 'Cause if you say you're going to wait until you have the money to take your kids about, they'll be grown up and gone. And it's just too late. So it's realizing in the first place that the opportunities are there for you, and having confidence to go for them.

BLACK IDENTITY

YVETTE: I was at someone's house last week, an old friend of mine. He was saying his sister goes skiing. Now my sister goes skiing, his attitude is only white people do things like that. Well, why shouldn't she go skiing? If she feels she wants to try it out and see what it's like? I mean, the world is her oyster, she can do anything she wants. She's an able-bodied person. Why not? But to put her down and make her feel she's 'un-Black' to want to go skiing? Nobody but nobody is going to tell me what I should do. The white man imposes, restricts my lifestyle enough, given half a chance. I'm not going to make it easy for him and be pushed into a slot. As Yvette, never mind about anything else. And it really makes me angry when other Black people try to do that to me as well.

I think it's lack of confidence. I really think it is. It isn't something that can be shown up so obviously but I think if you actually sat down and spoke to them, that's what you'd find. They don't feel they have a right to do things. It's something to do with people not being aware of the fact that they have rights as an individual, Black or white, rights that they must assume and use whichever way they want.

Because you are Black, you are immediately put into a category. Immediately. You can't be Black and middle-class and that is what really angers me. I use it to my advantage sometimes because I walk into meetings and people immediately assume all sorts of things and I just take over. Then they have to stop and think. But it really does make me angry. Anywhere I go, as soon as I walk in, I am a Black woman so therefore I am one, working-class, two, unintelligent, three, you know, the list is there, and then when you open your mouth, then they have to start reassessing.

I'm in social work, in adoption and fostering: I meet a lot of Black people in teaching, in social work, and I meet far fewer Black people doing things like interior design or something like that. There is something about me, about other Black people, who want to put something back for their own. I wouldn't be in social work if Black people had hardly any contact with those agencies. It's because Black people have so much interaction with social work agencies that I wanted to go into social work. And, in a way, I can understand that, and in a way I'm glad, because we need to be in there fighting for our own. But on the other hand, in a way I had no choice. I couldn't look further afield because to me that was made the most important thing in my life. So if I had artistic qualities, I'd be hard pushed to convince myself that that's where I should be heading. Because, what would I actually be giving back to Black people? What would I be doing? I feel I ought to be doing something. Now it could have been that I would have been like this anyway, but I'll never know. And whilst, as I say, on the one hand, I'm glad that I am and that so many Black people are looking at these gaps in the system where many more of us need to be – they're very important places – by the same token, how much we also need designers and dentists. We need all types everywhere. And in a way it's a bit out of our control.

Some of my boys' friends went to New York a few years ago, and they came back and said, there are all these Black people!

This kid was really excited, I mean they want to go there and stay there! That was the biggest thing of the holiday, not that the temperature was 110 and they almost died from heatstroke. It was the fact that there were all these Black people there.

ZHANA: I think the main reason why programmes like 'Fame' are so popular over here is because Black people here are so starved of any Black images. I mean, American football – I came over here to get away from American football!

YVETTE: Yes, sometimes I watch things and I think, my God, but that's as an adult. My children really latch on to that. If they went to somewhere like the States, they wouldn't want to come back!

I mean, my son, when he was six, we were looking through holiday brochures and he said, 'What's the matter with these places, don't Black people ever go on holiday?' And this is six years old. When he was three, and this is years ago, *Superman* came out and he was saying how he wanted to go see *Superman* and I said okay, and he said yeah he was gonna be Superman when he grows up, and I said fine, and he said yeah the first Black Superman. And it was those things that I realized that without pumping the kids constantly, because of the family, because of the way they see us conduct ourselves, the sort of people we have links with, they are very aware of themselves as Black people. So much so that the headmaster was challenged just last week for the third time. It wasn't the headmaster's fault, but he's dealt with the problem. But he had to, because my nine-year-old was saying, 'This book – this is how it makes me feel.' But it takes an awful lot of confidence for children to do that. And I think it's a lot to ask of them.

Friends of mine have been very surprised, but for me it's exactly what I want. But I didn't want to ruin their whole childhood by pumping it into them in a very obtuse manner. But at the same time, they've very much picked it up.

White Women

I remember when I was on my course three years ago I challenged a white woman in the group about her racism. She actually started crying, which had absolutely no effect on me whatsoever. Because, if I'm to cry for all the pain this country has caused me, I wouldn't stop. So, if she wants to cry once in awhile, it does 'er good. But why she started crying is that she admitted to our tutorial group that she didn't actually see me as a person. She sees me as this Black, um, 'thing' really. There's one or two things she said at the beginning when we all met, in our first tutorial session together, about eleven of us in the tutorial group. And by the time we met the third or fourth time, she really used to nark me. And I realized she didn't see me as Yvette having to get the shopping, having to take care of kids, having to anything. She just saw me as this very looming black object and that's all I was. She couldn't think of me as a human being living a day-to-day life, facing some of the other pressures she faces like, 'How am I going to pay this electricity bill?' I wasn't a human being to her. And that really really annoyed me and I challenged her about it and she admitted it in the end. 'Cause I wasn't gonna let go. And then she burst into tears. But I thought, you know, all right, so she admitted it, but that is the same for an awful lot of white people. An awful lot.

ZHANA: Yes, they see us as some kind of 'monolith'. We're not meant to be fully human. I call it the Cult of the Strong Black Woman. We're always expected to be tough, we're never allowed to be weak or vulnerable in any way.

YVETTE: That's right. We're not allowed to be. We've got nowhere to turn. We're not gonna get any sympathy from anybody.

That came up a lot, again when I was on the course, we went away for a few days to Kent. There were only twenty-five black students and about twenty came so it was 20/70 Black to white. And the majority of the Black students on the course were women. We were talking about sexism and a couple of us went to the tutor who was organizing it before we left and said, you know, if we're gonna talk about sexism, we have to talk about racism too. And he was saying, oh no no no, we'll deal with that another time. Okay, well, by the end of the four days and three nights at this university, the Black students had taken over. There were people having mini-breakdowns, and all this ridiculous business, you know. White women couldn't handle this business and how heavy it all was. Because the way these white women were talking, these so-called trendy white women who had it sorted out and whose men were so terrible, they were talking about men doing to them what they as white women do to me all the time and we're not sisters. We were not sisters. I haven't got any white sisters. How could I have? These women were going back to men who they were married to, or had large houses, they had home helps, they were comfortable women. But they wanted to identify with me as a Black woman. And for me to fight for their cause. Their experience is very different. To me, if all I had to worry about was what the white woman is worrying about, life would be kosher. But I've got that as a woman and racism as well. And I really haven't got time to hear about how tough life is for them. And they are part of the reason why it is so tough for me, too. If they could just see it.

A lot of the white women are saying about men dominating them and not seeing them as human beings, that they're achieving and have pride and that they have a role within the home but also outside, something to give society. And as far as I'm concerned, white women are in many ways a bigger enemy to me than the white man. Because I come into more contact with white women. And the thing is that it's a devil you never really know. They will agree with you on this and that. But I cannot see in my lifetime a white woman stepping to my side of the line against her white man. Oh, no, I'd never believe it. And until she's prepared to do that, she could never be anywhere near my sister, because she is still wanting her foot in both camps. She wants to be accepted because here's a conscious Black woman, well she's right-on, you see, if she has me for a friend. She must be okay, she doesn't have to work at it anymore. Yvette has given her a pass, so she's okay. And it's just not as simple as that – I don't trust them. See, I know I can't trust the white man. I know that already. And that's clear, there's no problem. But with a white woman who's saying all the right things, who is behaving in the right way, you can allow your defences to drop. And that can be your biggest mistake sometimes.

ZHANA: White men aren't always going on about 'brotherhood' or 'sisterhood'.
YVETTE: That's right! It's clear lines. That's why I say the devil you know. But with white women I feel that it's the devil that I don't really know. 'Cause they get too close sometimes and then you realize that you've actually let your defences down just that little bit, and it's been to your cost.

I had very little time for women on my course, who were mainly very middle-class white women.

Black Women

One of my issues is around Black people's attitudes to me and that is again why I tend to be a bit of a loner. I find – this is getting very very deep – a lot of it is Black women.

Just Friday, I attended a meeting, I came home and I said to my boyfriend, 'I think I've made another enemy.' And it was to do with jealousy, it was to do with ageism

There was a Black woman there, she was a bit older than me and there's the age thing about having respect for your elders which is still very much part of me. She was in her forties I suppose, not quite old enough to be my mother. But certainly an older Black woman, and immediately one would be respectful of that. But she's also in the line of work that I do.

This woman wouldn't look across at me – she'd never met me before, she'd only heard about me. She was on one side of the table, I was on the other, and I'd try and get her into the conversation, pick up on one or two things she said, not to criticize, just to elaborate or clarify, something like that. And she wouldn't look at me, it was all body language. She would turn sideways, she wouldn't look at me. Although I was talking to *her*, she wouldn't look at me. And plus, there were one or two things that were said in my favour at the meeting. I thought, maybe she feels she isn't being regarded enough from this person that she's never seen before in her life.

I challenged her at one point, when she started talking about one of the forms we use in our work. It's a form that we use when we assess families for fostering and adoption. And she was saying there's a group of Black workers now redesigning the form. Now, I agree that the format is a bit outdated now, needs to be revamped. But she was saying that, if you give this form to Black families, they're not going to understand it, they can't relate to it and blah de blah de blah. And I just thought, look, we have got to be careful 'cause we are at the risk of stereotyping *ourselves*. Here's this Black worker saying to these white people, Black people won't understand a form like this, it's too complicated. And I'm thinking, don't go telling them that. Because then I get angry if they think I haven't got the brain power to take in complex issues.

Well, in the end, I was saying goodbye to everybody and she totally ignored me. And I just feel that I've probably made a bit of an enemy. I think she saw me as this woman that she's never seen before, who's being regarded by other people at the meeting. Fair enough, I mean I've been there longer than she has, they know me, they don't know her except by reputation. And she saw me as a threat, as competition. Which I find *so sad*. And I've met it before. I met it on the course. And it's – I don't know what to do about it. It's not – I could even understand if I were a pompous person who kept myself apart. But I love my people so much. I'm to the point of naïve in that, as far as I'm concerned, if you're Black then I want to talk to you at the canteen. I want to sit next to *you*! If you're the only other Black person at that conference, I'm making a beeline for you at the tea break. To that point, because if you're on your own, I'm on my own, it's not because I lack confidence, I can hold my own. But I want you to recognize that I actually regard you as an important person here. By the mere fact that you're Black, if you're the only other person then you and I *must* sit down for lunch together. Things like that are important to me. I never want to be seen as one of these people who – you know Black people aspire, and they forget about others. I can't relate to that at all, I can't! My family would bring me back down to earth if I did that, anyway, thank God. But I can't relate to that. And I don't want other Black people to see me like that. But I feel that I do get myself pushed into this position. More so by women, other Black women, that they have created this position for themselves and if another Black woman comes along who's seen as bright or whatever, they feel that they're automatically threatened. Instead of thinking, hey, let's join forces, let's be strong together, there's two of us now to take them all on, they see us as a threat, that I'm going to threaten their domain, which hurts me very, very much.

I think it's a question of Black women in particular not being able to achieve certain things, now being put in a position to actually have a say in what happens, have a bit of power, and they don't want anybody to threaten that at all. Why does it have to be seen as a threat?

The Black women at work that I tend to relate to are the ones that don't see that as an issue. If I'm there and they're there, then we automatically try to get on. But I felt it was a shame because that woman, I didn't feel that toward her. I actually felt a link because she was Black. I don't care how naïve that sounds. Because she was a Black woman in a predominantly white meeting, and I was a Black woman there, I automatically had a respect for her until she shows me that she doesn't deserve it. And I wanted to make that sort of link with her. But the way she came across very early on made me feel so uncomfortable and – I don't even feel angry about it. I feel sad about it. That was worse than white people not wanting you. That was worse. That really does make me feel so sad.

And I just left that meeting feeling, oh, God, you know, I don't want to get on the wrong side of somebody, but I did absolutely nothing to her. I mean, just my mere presence wasn't good from her point of view. As far as she was concerned, her mind was made up. There's nothing I can do about it except play it straight down the line, pretend I haven't noticed and continue and hope that in time she'll realize that she has nothing to be afraid of.

I think I've come to being a bit of a loner. Because I won't change myself. However sad it makes me, I'm not going to change myself because that's *me*.

I come into contact with Black women's groups through the course of my work. I tend to go out and talk to them, I don't allow myself to be office-bound, because I hate that. And particularly if you're from the Caribbean, there is almost a cult that if you're a Black conscious woman, you're supposed to have a particular look about you for one thing, you're supposed to behave in a certain way. And again, it goes back to the fact that I won't allow anybody to tell me – I have to be what I feel most comfortable with. And there's this suspicion that I feel sometimes when I meet other Black women – for one thing, I think, because I speak very English. I've been here since I was three, my parents were Guyanese, so, um, they spoke with a Guyanese accent, obviously, but they were city people as well. So, they didn't have countrified speech.

When I went to secondary school, it was one of the first comprehensives. And I was in the top stream for my first year. And I remember passionately – the majority of Black kids were in lower streams. And so we never came in contact with each other apart from the playground. I remember *desperately* wanting to be accepted by that group, I mean, it was the most important thing in my first and second year. And they would be together at one end of the playground, I'll always remember, by the benches. And they'd sit and chat and they'd be very friendly and everything. And I always thought, me and a few others, we couldn't get in. Because we were seen as bright, we were in the top stream, they never met us any other way apart from in the playground. I wanted to be accepted so desperately. I wanted them to like me, I wanted to be part of them 'cause I was Black too. But a lot of the time, when they were together, they would talk in patois. And I couldn't follow it because my parents never spoke it. I can do it now because I taught myself! I was determined. Even now, it doesn't sound natural. I think anybody who really speaks it would know straightaway. But I remember passionately I wanted so much to be accepted.

I never was, I might add. It never did come off. At the time I didn't realize what a passion it was, but thinking back over the years, I think, those girls were my whole life. I wanted so much to be accepted by them. And I'd get comments like, because I was in the top stream, oh, 'You think you're too clever for us', and things like that. I didn't! I thought they were *wonderful* people, I wanted to be *like them*. Now I look back, I'm glad I wasn't! Because why should I have to be a particular type to be accepted? Why do I have to be in one of the bottom streams to be okay with Black people? But at the time, I wanted to be like them. And they'd say things like, they'd say I would pretend I couldn't follow their speech because I thought I was uppity. It had nothing to do with that whatsoever. I wasn't brought up in a house like that. Most of the kids were from Jamaica, you see. We're Guyanese.

It's not the sort of thing that you talk about to other people because they wouldn't always understand it.

[Speaking Patois] shouldn't be a prerequisite for being accepted. It shouldn't be something that I have to do. It made me feel left out, yes, it did. To be honest, I don't actually have any burning desire to be terrifically fluent in it, any more than I have a desire to do other things, but I just don't see why I *have* to be fluent in it to be accepted. If a group of Black women were saying to me, you'd have to be fluent in patois for us to accept you, then I don't *want* to be fluent because I'm not going to allow you to impose your restrictions on me. What about my principles? What about my politics? Are they nothing? I don't put on the way I speak. There are good reasons why I speak the way I do.

ZHANA: What happened at college?

YVETTE: I talk about this quite freely now, but it took me years and years to understand this. It happened on my course, in my first year, where it was myself and a friend that it happened to, and it just – I wasn't aware of it for a long time, the first two terms. The third term, I was so upset. That was one of the worst periods of my life. I was almost afraid to go in every day. And you're talking to someone who's pretty tough, even though I say it myself. It takes a lot to rock me. But apparently, I mean, I got the impression that I was *hated* with this ferocity. A couple of the women actually commented on the fact that I had three kids, and a husband who would never stand in the way of anything I wanted to do. And a couple of the women, when they had their blowouts with me, they said things that made it clear that they were jealous. I was very lucky. I know that. I had my family, I had my freedom. I was very lucky. And, also, some of the women on the course weren't as educated as I was. Not that I was terrifically educated, but I came from a family where from the time we were that high, we had books and were encouraged to think politically. So it came naturally and there was a lot of jealousy about that. I remember one woman who lived in Brixton and she would bring out her Brixton experiences at every point, as if, because she lived in Brixton, she knew what being Black was about and I didn't.

I never used to say an awful lot. If I said something, then I was showing off. If I didn't say enough, then I was sitting back to let the others do the work – I mean, you couldn't win. By no means the whole group, but it was the stronger members of the group. And they were the ones who set the pitch.

Some were quiet, and allowed the others, a handful, to do this. But they were the quieter ones, anyway, who wouldn't have challenged the more vocal members. And it was, of course, the more vocal members who carried the swing. I remember being so upset and so hurt by their attitude, and it was again very much this narrowing thing that I was 'un-Black' because I wasn't A, B, C and D.

It was very painful, but it's made me very aware of the power that I hold as far as other Black women see it. I don't see myself as particularly powerful, but they see it as that I've got *enormous* power. And they're often threatened. It is something that I've come up against, and certainly visiting Black women's groups, I think before I go in the door, I wonder what their reaction will be. For one, I come from Social Services. For two, I speak in a particular way. For three, I don't wear a turban on my head. You know, all these sorts of things that I'm supposed to do to be right on. And yet, I'm sure if you actually put it down on paper, politically I'm far more aware, far more conscious, on all sorts of levels, than they are. But they're not seeing that at first.

Make-up is a big issue, certainly with Black women who are supposed to be conscious. Hair used to be, less so now, I must admit. It's moved on an awful lot. Certainly with Black men who make comments like, 'Why do you have to put all that stuff on your face?' And yet they'll go out with a white woman who's wearing gallons of the stuff. And I think, what are you trying to –

ZHANA: In Africa, women have worn cosmetics from time immemorial.

YVETTE: That's right. And, I mean, that's my individual right. It's my face. It's got nothing to do with anybody else anyway. I just think, blow it, that's it. But that doesn't mean that I'm not aware of the reactions I might get. But I think, blow it. I won't allow myself to be limited. If I want a big house in the country, then I'll get a big house in the country. I don't have to live in Brixton to prove how Black I am.

To do something successfully, and to really put your heart in it, you have to be happy within yourself. If you are being restricted by other people's judgments, you're not going to be totally happy.

I think it's changing. I find young Black girls around here have moved on an awful lot from when I was little. Particularly around things like processing your hair and things like that, you know, straightening it or not straightening it. Black women nowadays, particularly the younger ones, teenage and early twenties, are much more inclined towards either wet-looking their hair and then straightening it the next three months, then plaiting it the next three months. You know, you just do what you want. I do that. Changing the style depending on what mood takes me. It's not so much seen as 'un-Black' to do it now. When I was growing up, it was the Afro. That's all you could do, really. I wore an Afro all the time.

I don't allow [disapproval] to restrict what I want to do and I will just continue, in some ways, as if I don't actually realize it's there and just hope that people accept me before they actually start to judge me too deeply.

There's the whole thing that, if you straighten your hair, then you're trying to emulate the white woman. When I was growing up, in the late Sixties, early Seventies, there was this very conscious American influence of Black power and Black rights and civil rights and all the rest of it. It was very much – the Afro was a statement. And if you didn't wear an Afro, then, what the hell were you, really? You weren't Black. You're not saying you're Black because you're not showing it physically in your hairstyle. The fact that people would go through, I mean, chemicals weren't as refined as they are nowadays so people were almost burning their scalp for it to be straightened or, you know, curly style. And there was a lot of bad feeling towards women who did do that. We were denying our Africanness. Verbally. Nobody would cut anybody's hair or anything like that. But you would be told, literally. But also there was the subtle side that, even if you wanted to, you wouldn't dare because you wouldn't dare the reaction afterwards. So you just kidded yourself that what you actually wanted was an Afro, even if it didn't suit the shape of your face, you wore it all the time and you made sure you ended up liking it. Very few of my group in those days wore their hair in anything other than an Afro.

It's based on the spirit that made you question – to think back, I remember being more on the side of the ones who would question people who straighten their hair than the other side who would be very sort of understanding about it. In those teenage years, I was getting terribly conscious of my identity and being very aware of what was happening to me and what had previously happened. Those were very formative years. And, whilst I wouldn't ignore somebody who maybe straightened their hair, it did make me question where they were coming from, and wonder. Nine times out of ten, once you got to know them, it wasn't an issue. I was very influenced, in those days, by a lot of material I used to read. Malcolm X, Angela Davis. But then, as I got older and stronger, I thought, well, what the hell? People do what they want to do. The thing is, for me, is that I do realize that there are Black people who do things to their hair because they want to look a certain way. Black men included. I'm just as happy to have my hair in lots of little plaits, which I constantly do. If you met somebody who knew me, that's the first image that they would probably picture, Yvette in plaits rather than anything else. But if I don't want to wear it like that, and I want to wear it straightened, then I will, three months on. But my politics have not changed. And anybody who thinks they have is making a grave mistake if they try to challenge me on it.

I deal with a lot of young Black women who wear their hair straight and some of them, fair dues, it's because it's easier and because it's fashionable and it's in. But some of them, it's because they actually don't like that kink, where they straighten their hair to such extremes. It's very difficult to know where their denial of their Blackness and their love of their own Black hair stops and something else begins. It's very, very difficult, because most of them would say, 'Of course we love our hair in its natural state, but it's just that we feel like having it like this now.'

Make-up bothers me more. [*A prominent Black public figure*] wears blues, greens and everything on her eyes and she wears it so heavily and I think, well, hey, you're such a pretty woman anyway, you don't need all of that. But then, to be honest, if I saw a white woman on the train the same I'd think, Oh my God. It is more to do with excess than Blackness. And it is so unusual to see Black women piling it on like that that you sort of think, God, what's going on?

The one thing that does annoy me and I still hear it, not so much as I used to but it's when you get Black people, particularly older ones, who talk about children who've got 'good' hair. Oh, God! That really kills me! My hair is *wonderful*! I think my boys have *wonderful* hair! But it's not what would usually be termed 'good hair'. I mean, that's a dead giveaway as far as I'm concerned.

To see a Black woman, she's got her hair straightened, because it's straightened it's usually longer, I mean, used to cause such an extreme reaction – you know – 'You think you're white, you're this, you're that'. It's that sort of attitude.

ZHANA

African Women on a Postcard

Once, the woman told me, they'd traded amongst themselves. Bartered maize for cassava, livestock for some land or for a bribe. The old woman leaned back and grunted. She was spared the heavy work now. These days, her main duty was to oversee the daily process of pounding the cassava.

The women reached their arms up, then brought them heavily thudding down again in a rhythm which calmed the babies to sleep and made background music for the stories they told to pass the time. The old woman continued, 'I remember when my husband came to pay my bride price and took me away. He brought a cow along with the usual goats and chickens. My father was very pleased, but I ran and hid. I was young then, and foolish.'

I watched the women, the way they walked, their faces sometimes laughing, sometimes angry. I thought, that one could have been my sister, that one my cousin or my next-door-neighbour. I thought of the women in Deptford, in Oxford Street or in New York City, the way they moved pushing a pram, instead of carrying a baby on their hips. Arms loaded with shopping were here traded for jugs of water balanced on the head. But the walk was basically the same.

I couldn't understand the language the women spoke. I'd studied for eighteen months to learn the rudiments of Arabic, which they used when they deigned to communicate with me. But most of the time, they spoke their own tongue, ignoring me, the outsider. I was eager to hear the old woman's story, to get this rare glimpse of her life.

Tomorrow was market day. After the women finished pounding the cassava, and fetched the water, collected some firewood, built a fire and started their evening meal, they'd begin packing. Brightly coloured fabrics they'd spun by hand, and woven on their house looms. These skirts always went down well with the tourists. Hand-carved necklaces, pottery, statues went into the baskets. All these would be traded for gold, and maybe a bit of jewellery for themselves. Gold could pay for their sons' education, gold could buy a big car for their husband or a house in the city and, when they'd saved up enough, gold would pay for a new dress or suit from London or Paris.

* * *

UMA
Oral History

* * *

Introduction

Uma, a woman of Indian-subcontinent descent, was born in Fiji and grew up in Aotearoa (New Zealand). Her background as a working-class descendant of migrant labourers has shaped her politics. Although in Aotearoa the Maori population is only 12%, and in Aboriginaland (Australia), the Aboriginal population is only 1% of the total, the fact that in other parts of the Pacific there is only a tiny percentage of whites and a large population of Indian, Chinese and other Pacific peoples means that Pacific women are not restricted to living in white-dominated societies.

The experience of Black people in the Pacific informs our own. In addition to the obvious links with the struggle for land rights and self-determination for indigenous peoples, there are less obvious parallels. For example, the Pacific experience of living with the nuclear threat has made the link between racism and health-care issues undeniably clear.

Because she has spent her life in societies where there was enormous cultural diversity in terms of languages, religions, belief systems, etc, it comes naturally to Uma to respect others' differences. However, she has always been seen as the 'other' by the members both of the predominantly white Australian feminist and gay movements and of the Asian professional classes who have been allowed to migrate to Aboriginaland.

On coming to Britain, Uma experienced being ostracized by Black women, including Asian lesbians, who also chose to label her as 'other'.

UMA: I feel that it is important that each of us places herself in context for ourselves and each other, for only then can we know where we're coming from and where we're at. In other words, by recognizing and acknowledging our experiences and how they have shaped us, and why our 'life-styles', politics, ideology and beliefs are what they are. So I would like to share with you a little about myself and my background.

My people were from the rural areas of Rajasthan. They were taken as indentured labourers from Northern India to work in the sugar-cane plantations in the land of the Fijian people in the South Pacific. Two generations of my people were born there and when I was a baby my parents migrated to Aotearoa, the land of the Maori people. For ten years I lived in the land of the Aboriginal people – 'Australia'. Currently I am living and working in England. I identify as a Womanist and a Zami. I am a descendant of Woman Healers and am a Healer myself. My primary commitment is liberation struggles of Black and Indigenous/Native peoples and I am involved in the Nuclear Free and Independent Pacific Movement. The need for my skills is vitally important for we are struggling to survive in the midst of a nuclear war that has been waged on/over/about us for over forty years. I know that it is a risk to say so much about myself. It makes me even more vulnerable not only to criticism but also because we are being watched by the forces of the evil powers that govern us. They would not hesitate to try to eliminate any one of us, the minute they deem us as too much of a threat to them.

I know that it is crucially important that we network internationally and work together in coalition. However, I believe that we have to constantly balance what the commonalities among us may be, with what the very real differences are. We must examine what assumptions we make; what we take for granted; what our priorities are; what our expectations of ourselves and each other are and on whose terms we operate. We must challenge each other, for ultimately we are all accountable to each other. But most especially those most privileged are accountable to the most oppressed. The personal is still political and vice-versa. [From the magazine, *Mother Tongue*.]

ZHANA: Tell me what your perceptions were of Britain before you came.

UMA: First of all, I didn't have – there wasn't as much stuff coming out. So, in fact, I knew there were Black people here, obviously. It was obvious for me because I work things out and I'm not surprised when people – you know, I knew there were Black people here. And it stands to reason to me, if there were Black people here, there were Black people fighting back. Now, if there were Black people fighting back, there were going to be women. All liberation struggles actually are the work of women, predominantly the work of women. So I knew that there would be women. Now, if there were going to be Black women, then there were going to be women loving women. So I thought, even though I wasn't maybe having that writing coming over here, meaning in Sydney, where I was at the time, there must be Black women. And I was seeing some articles, glimpses in things like *Spare Rib*. And then later, I got to see one or two rare copies of *Outwrite*. So I knew then. So that's the picture I had. I knew they were there somewhere. I had to find them. If there was one of me here, there couldn't be less than one person there. So, and then I arrived and I knew I was right. And I thought, now, how do I locate the others? And just what will be the most sensible places to start meeting some of the people?

It was incredibly exciting for me to see so many Black people. People complain, there aren't so many, percentagewise. But you've got to understand, there's still a higher percentage for me visually. For me, to have my face, my colour, my everything external reflected back to me is something I don't think that people who haven't gone through it understand.

I did travel through Southeast Asia, so I did see Black people. But, I was still stared at. I was still different. Because I moved, walked, talked differently. So I was still the outsider. The thing I felt visually, just on the streets here, in a sense, that I hadn't felt, for instance, when I was in Bombay, was that the way I dressed and moved myself appeared, at least at that initial level, at that initial point, much more similar. So, I felt fairly comfortable in Brixton, for example. Less comfortable in Southall, interestingly enough.

ZHANA: Why is that?

UMA: I think because Brixton is more similar to the Black areas at home. I haven't grown up with predominantly Indian communities around me. So, for me, on a very personal level, when I'm seeing people of African descent, and also island people, Afro-Caribbean island people, some things are similar. That was something I'd grown up with. And certainly for me, growing up in Auckland – remember, Auckland is the largest Pacific-island city in the world. So that you have lots of people from the islands, and the other thing is, of course, it's a warm country so people can actually wear their clothing and their style of dress on the streets. So you walk down and you see them. So sometimes, you know, in Brixton, in the warm weather – hah! – people were, actually came, dressed, you know. And the ambience is a bit more similar, you know, like the marketplace, people calling out and singing, stuff like that.

And also, although I didn't get the writing of Black women, I did, of course, because we are dominated, we are a British-colonized country. We had American media, but we also had information from Britain. So there were British newspapers, British news, British television programmes and stuff. So you did start seeing Black people in them. So that, even though it was a minor bit, it was a glimpse. And if you knew that –

ZHANA: Okay, so you knew that these Black women were out there somewhere. You came and you started finding them. Initially, how did you perceive them, and how did they perceive you?

UMA: I can only hazard a guess as to how they perceived me. Some people have told me.

ZHANA: What did they do? How did they respond? What kind of questions did they ask you about where you came from?

UMA: Well, in fact, very few people bothered to ask me, which was sad, because I could have put them straight. Now, first of all, in terms of perceptions, I saw lots of beautiful Black women on the streets, in the areas. And in terms of wanting to be around politicized women, I thought, I'd like to start sussing out from an aspect of the movement that I recognize. So I went to AWP, A Woman's Place, which was, I felt, the central focus or central information point for the white women's movement. And so I went to suss out what was happening. So I hung around there a lot. I also knew the Brixton Black Women's Centre, and I had the feeling that that was the Black women and AWP was the white women. So I went to Brixton Black Women's Centre to start finding out what was happening, what was going on. Now one of the things that I found very sad in some ways, and that was very painful for me to experience, was that many people instantly said, 'Oh, I didn't realize – what accent is that?' And I'd be vague, I'd say it was Kenya or something. And some of them would pick it up and say, 'Oh, it's Australian,' and I would say, 'Well, almost Australian.' Well, anyway, lots of people would say, 'Oh! A Black woman from Australia! I didn't know there were Black women in Australia.' And I felt so upset. Because, one, I'd have to explain that I wasn't actually a Black woman from Australia. Not only wasn't I born there, but I wasn't from there, and that there actually were Aboriginal people. And that was part of the pain, of Black people not even knowing the existence of our people and how horrible that is, that annihilation, the non-existence of a people. So that was painful but, of course, it did allow me the opportunity to actually talk about the existence of peoples in the Pacific. So that was the first thing in terms of how I was perceived. I was perceived as a Black woman from Australia. And so all the assumptions that go with that on both sides.

ZHANA: Wasn't it partly, though, the fact that Black people over here don't perceive Aboriginal people as Black? Because I think that we are aware that there are still some Aboriginal people left.

UMA: You see, that's the other thing. How people could not recognize that Black people in Australia are Black. I find that just so stunning. In fact, I can in some ways handle better that, to some Black people, they will not accept that people from the Indian subcontinent, on their terms, are Black. Okay, we could argue about that, but the point is, there is some point where you can start to see that. But I cannot give any validity to the idea that people who are Aboriginal aren't Black. Look, do your homework. Have a look. *Look* at the people. You cannot look at the people and say they're not Black. Their experiences of slavery and enslavement, the fact that it's happened in their own land, is the same. Do you deny that people in South Africa are Black? And physically. *Physically*, you know, the people are Black!

ZHANA: Yes, all of that, I totally accept all of that. But I know that, when I came to this country, I had reservations because in the States, Blackamericans are not accepted by Westindians. And a lot of Blackamericans don't perceive Westindians as being Black. It's nothing to do with the way they look or their experience of slavery or anything like that. It's because of the way they behave. And I didn't know, when I came here, whether I'd be accepted. Because a lot of Westindians in the States do not identify themselves with the Black community.

UMA: You see, that's something I hadn't thought of. Because of the way they behave.

ZHANA: And that's why I would not have perceived Aborigines as Black. Because I wouldn't know if they would accept me or want to identify with me.

UMA: That's interesting, isn't it? Because I found, in fact, that Black people over here didn't act Black according to what I was thinking of as Black. So it was working the other way as well. I'd think, 'If they're Black people, why are they doing – ?' The one thing that, to me, was something that I always thought of as 'Black', as part of my Black identity, was hospitality. At home, hospitality is a totally different thing with Black people. To arrive over here and to find the inhospitality of Black people just blew me away. It was a contradiction that I could not understand. Certainly not when I first arrived. Having been here a lot longer, I understand that this country does in Black people's heads. But at that point, I would have thought that, if they came over and came on like that, you couldn't have seen them as being Black. Or you'd see them as someone who was very ill. They were suffering from some kind of illness and needed to get well again. And I think that's true because living here – that's what I meant – you're suffering from psychic illness. And, as I said, it manifests itself around issues of hospitality.

So, yes, I hadn't thought about it the other way around, about the behaviour. But then, culturally, rural lifestyles, indigenous lifestyles, I think they would have to examine that in a totally different way. If Blackamericans acknowledge say, for example, that their roots are African, then understanding African cultures within the context of Africa, there is a similarity with Aboriginal culture. Then, if you're going back like that, in terms of what is Blackness, then that's what I'm saying, that even culturally, the behaviour of today among Aboriginal people is definitely identifiably Black.

I must admit that, for lots of people, my behaviour was something they couldn't understand or couldn't accept. It wasn't white – the closest white people they knew were Australians – but it wasn't, in their terms, Black. Now, the funny part of it is, in the Australian context, I'm not seen as being a white Australian in my behaviour. So I found it quite strange when I was labelled a Black Australian. And they were saying 'Black Australian' meaning 'Black white Australian person'. Oooh, yuck! Because I didn't see myself as being anything like *them* in any way, shape or form, one hopes! So I was labelled as brash. So that meant I was loud, noisy, assertive, and those things were not acceptable –

ZHANA: Since when are Black women not supposed to be loud, noisy and assertive?

UMA: And the other thing was, I had put up with it for years around the white movement, that I was a personality and it was their problem. To suddenly find myself in an all-Black-women context, to see the same thing, this was another time I was blown away. They could not pay attention to anything I was saying because of the way I said it or the way I was behaving, in their eyes, behaving. I was just being. But it's like, you're not going to listen to someone because they're wearing yellow instead of red.

ZHANA: They're so British now. They're so bloody British! It doesn't matter what you do to people – look at what the British have done to people all over the world. But because they're polite, because they had tea at four, therefore it was cool.

UMA: You see, that was the other thing, that, if you didn't like what I was doing or how I was behaving, then I was quite prepared for someone to say, 'Hey, I don't like that', or 'Why'd you stand on my foot', basically. Then I'd say, 'I didn't realize I was standing on your foot.' And if that's what it feels like for the person, I might make some effort to take my foot away. But because of that being polite and not being straight-out, listen, I didn't know what was going on. And so there was a basic dishonesty going on there. In the end, I felt like I had BO of some kind, which no one would tell me about. Because I'd rush up to someone and say 'Hi!!' And they would go 'Aaaahh!!!' [*deep breath, backs off*], you know? And I'd feel absolute horror and embarrassment and sometimes rage.

The other side was, as well, I came over here bouncing with enthusiasm and all this, and I came to share. I feel I have been politically active, I have learnt this much, I'm involved in front-line struggles over there. I wanted to meet the Black peer group. The attitude was that, um, all of us are ignorant, London is the political navel of the world, the sisters here have done it all, I couldn't possibly know. And, I was told that I was behaving like – now, this is something you'll have to sort out – that Blackamerican people are always telling Black British people how to conduct their struggles. And I was saying, that is something you'll have to sort out. But you've got to understand that I didn't come from a context of a big world power like the US. I'm coming from the other end. In fact, you're living in a place that's colonized us. So, I've got very real things to say. And, no, I didn't come to sit here at the feet of anybody, you know, to learn in that kind of way.

ZHANA: I've very much come across that attitude, 'We were involved in the Brixton sisters, we were involved in this, that and the other, so therefore we've got it all sussed out' – you know – 'We've been meeting for ten years, we all know each other's first names, and you're an outsider, so you don't know anything, so you'd better shut up and listen.' And the difference with me was because I was from the States, I was very conscious of the attitude that Americans always take over everything. And I was really quiet. I went to listen, I went to learn. And a few months ago, I started thinking, well, God, I'm so much more aware now. How could I have been so ignorant when I first came over? Then I started realizing, I wasn't *at all* ignorant when I came over here. I just had a different experience.

UMA: You just had a different reality. Yeah. The other thing was, I don't think they actually wanted you to listen. They want you to hear what they're saying, but not to listen, because, in fact, they didn't recognize the fact that I *was* listening, I was paying attention, and I was giving them immediate feedback about what was being said. And they did not recognize that. All they wanted to recognize is – they wanted me to shut up. And I think to myself, right. In some other context, in a very narrow context sometimes, I am a Womanist, okay? And I'm a Black feminist lesbian. And I'm with other Black feminist lesbians, right? And we're talking. Well, they're talking, I'm supposed to pay attention. And some of the stuff is about making worldwide affiliations with Black women everywhere. And I think, how? How are you going to make alliances with another sister when she doesn't speak the same language as you, doesn't live culturally in any way, shape or form like you? How can you make alliances with someone like that if you can't even do it with me? If you're finding me a problem? And then also, the other thing is, on whose terms are we going to make the alliances? For me, what I've experienced is intense imperialism of people here, and Black people here as well, towards Black peoples from other parts of the world, and particularly from what I prefer to call first nation, what's called third world. That has to be recognized. Because, as Black people, we do need to work together. But we have to keep examining on whose terms we're working together.

We've also got to realize that our being multilingual is an asset, not a problem, right. But I find it very difficult to really understand how people who politically are sussed out on so many levels, and understand how oppression works, can turn around and not recognize what's happening.

ZHANA: I think a lot of people do recognize it, but then they sit there and say, 'Yes, we've got this problem, but I'm not actually part of the problem, I'm part of the solution' – you know.

UMA: Some of the people do that. A lot of the people don't even get to first base.

ZHANA: I've been to so many Black women's conferences where we've sat down and said, 'Okay, let's discuss definitions of being

Black,' and it just ends up in a slanging match. And to me, that is just a perpetuation of the problem. But people think that they're actually coming up with the solution. That we only have to sit down and define our terms now.

UMA: The thing is, I think that we've gotta find a balance between what the differences are, because we have to examine the differences, and what those differences mean, and not make assumptions about them; we've got to balance that with what the commonalities are. Because sometimes we forget either one of those. We've gotta look at what we take for granted, what assumptions we make, all sorts of things. And we've gotta continue dialoguing. There's no point saying, 'Well, I don't want to wish to talk to her any more' or 'I don't wanna listen to her 'cause she ain't got the right perfume on.' I have seen the politics of pettiness operate here. And the politics of privilege. The politics of privilege is pettiness. And the thing is, we don't have the luxury. I'm sorry, we don't have the luxury to say, 'I don't want to . . . because.' If the sister is there and she's back-to-back with you, fighting them off, then you'd better get your act together and realize what that actually means.

And the other thing is, no, we also don't have the luxury to actually like each other. If we can like each other, that's wonderful. But if we can work together, that's more important. I'm not worried about liking people, and not being liked. It's very important for me to be respected. And I want respect. And I think that one of the things I found about being here is that I've come to recognize – heavy terms here – that this is an immoral place. That dishonesty is very rife and I think that one of the most deathly things, annihilating things, is cynicism. Cynicism is almost worshipped here. It's seen as being very cool. But, in fact, it's not. It's a death of the spirit. You know – what is the point, if you feel that cynicism?

And I think issues around language – and I'm speaking now in the context around women of Indian-subcontinent descent who are activists at a very high level – sometimes I think that because we are articulate in English, like I am, incredibly articulate in English, we can forget the reality of language and what it means.

There's a new booklet just come out, put out by the GLC Women's Committee, and there's a section in it called 'Black and Ethnic Minority Women'. I could not believe that those two pages did not once mention language. And yet language is *crucial.* It's crucial around *English*, let alone looking at other languages.

The other issue that's of deep concern to me, and I've come to recognize just how serious the issue is, and that is, addiction. I'm not even talking around the larger sense as we know it. But it's around the addiction within the Black-feminist, Black-lesbian-feminist community. We are failing to actually address ourselves to that issue – if a sister is in a situation where she should feel less of a need to turn to any other external supports outside of herself, if she's got the active support of the sisters around her. But in fact, that's not so. There is no open forum, or even a small forum, of accountability, of saying to someone, 'Hey, I felt really upset and pissed off and hurt that you didn't turn up or you didn't do such-and-such.' To actually say to someone outright, challenging, 'Why did you say such-and-such at this mixed meeting? I couldn't challenge you there.' But there doesn't seem to be the desire to challenge each other, to see each other as accountable to each other, and then having done that, to also take it from there, to actually be concerned. You know, it isn't funny that so-and-so is never seen without a can of some particular brand name of beer in her hand. Or she's always got a little bottle of whisky and it's said half-jokingly because it's a 'tough' thing to do. And then also not recognizing the fact – I mean, okay, you know, ganja is taken. But at the level at which it's taken, people who at all times are stoned. And then there's all the heavy drugs, smack, etc. I think that's the other issue that I don't feel is examined enough. I think it's a *massive* issue. And how many sisters have already died? How many more are going to die before we, among ourselves, say, 'Hey, we're getting something wrong here.' Instead of having a lower level of addiction among ourselves when we're together, less desire to want to drink when I'm with you than when I'm out there, because of course we're going to say that the external problems aren't going away. And I understand that. What I'm saying is, when I'm with you, why do I still have this desire to want to get out of it? Women's health suffers, everything. We all suffer. If one of us is ill because of her addiction, all of us are, and we've got to see that. And we're not seeing it like that. So either you make a figure of fun of that person or try and make it a macho-type exciting thing to do, or it's a done thing and you, in fact, look down on someone who doesn't do those things. I know that there's a lot of fear operating.

I'm thirty-five, and I would like to be in a position where I can challenge the women who are my age-group. Not only because there are younger women who are going through that. Some of the women who are older have actually passed through that. What are they doing to offer support to the younger women? Letting them get on with it. It's almost like you can only become part of the inner sanctum if you're tough enough to survive all that. If not, well, it doesn't matter if you fall by the wayside. But there aren't enough of us, you know? And that completely blows my mind.

ZHANA: I don't even see it in terms of there not being enough of us. Our lives are precious. It doesn't matter how many of us there are.

UMA: That's right. Every one of us is incredibly precious.

ZHANA: Back to language. You were saying about how important it is. Can you clarify?

UMA: It's about constructive reality. You see, one of the things I've come to understand – see, I've never felt the Pacific identity as strongly as I have here. One of the benefits, and it's a major benefit, for me growing up where I did, was I grew up surrounded by peoples of all sorts of different cultures. It is true here in London. Right. How 'bout that? What isn't true here in London is that there is not much mixing and coming together and sharing and stuff like that. I'm not talking about melting pot here. I'm talking about salad. So that I grew up, as I said, surrounded by people – and I would be celebrating, going to whatever the festivals were, whether it was Eid, whether it was Diwali, you know. I'm sure if there had been Kwanzaa, we'd have been doing that. Whatever it was, we were celebrating together. And that's just a mark of it. We were in and out of each other's homes. So, for me I grew up with lots of different people believing different things. We all occupied the same space. So I don't have a problem that anyone has to believe in my reality, or my viewpoint or perspective of the world. The issue is when any one particular person sees theirs as the only way to be and all ours as wrong. And so that's part and parcel of stuff here. Now language is a major, important aspect of that because language is how you construct reality or make sense of reality and concepts of reality. It's not just that the people can't necessarily articulate in the English language. We can't articulate in the language they understand. For me, my understanding comes from the sheer fact of growing up with my mother, whose concepts are in a different language and culture. And I have trouble, we have trouble communicating. Not only across generation, but language. I've just gone to the trouble of writing a very crucial letter to my mother, which I've had written in the Hindi language because I want to get this issue across to her. And so, from that very basic understanding within my home situation, I have followed through to understanding the implications of that for lots of people.

This relates to women in Britain because of the thing about language and understanding, how you deal with reality, and what language you use to deal with it. So that, you know, the issues around mother-tongue teaching and retaining our cultures are tied up with language. And it's not simply that the problem will go away or disappear because more and more of our kids can speak English. It'll just go underground and be hidden. Because we ourselves are manifesting that in our lives. Because part and parcel of – okay, some of us, you know, of course there are generations of kids who are born and have grown up in this country who speak English, and English is part of their language, right? Every day there are new women, Black women, coming to this country, being in this country. And language is still an issue for them and for us. We ourselves may be subconsciously believing that's going to change. It isn't.

ZHANA: For me, it's more of an issue of trying to relearn what was taken from me.
UMA: Right. And then we've got people living here who have got those languages. Many of our sisters are bi-, tri-, you've got no idea how many languages they speak! It's just wonderful! But instead of seeing that as a richness, it's that schizophrenic thing. At the same time we're saying, 'We want to reclaim our heritage, we want to be able to learn this language,' there are sisters around us who speak it. And what do we do? We make them inconsequential. It's not inconsequential.

It's not just older women. There are women being married and brought into the country. And the thing is, there are very few services for women, as we know, very few services that cater to us. And the services that are set up on an alternative basis still cater to women who are English-speaking, if not monocultural and monolingual, at least English-speaking and understanding. And it's just the tip of that. And so we've got to do something about that. It's up to us who can articulate that. And I'm afraid that some of us, who are like me, forget that and forget that it's part of our responsibility to keep pushing that. To keep fighting in that area. And it's not just her issue, it's not just that who feels it knows it. That is true, but, at the same time, to me, I'm still feeling it in my life. And while we're not fighting, those of us who feel that don't fight that, then we're denying that. And you can go off to your classes or linguaphone and stuff like that, but, in fact, how can you deal with that schizophrenic experience of what's happening? It's only us who can do it, along with women who are non-English-speaking. Together we must fight that. And see that their access to those languages is something we could benefit from and that our access to the languages we have, particularly English, is something we can benefit from. And see that as a mutually beneficial thing, not see them as mutually exclusive.

I haven't seen enough about the issue around language, really. I mean, yes, of course, we're talking about having translations done. I think it's important that we have all the information translated into other languages. But we forget that there's information in those languages that should be translated in the other direction. That's the kind of thing we have to rethink and continue re-examining doing in that area. We have to prioritize language in a way that we haven't done fully enough. And particularly for me because, yes, of course it affects men, but for me, it means we're cut off from our mothers, our sisters, our daughters.

ZHANA: Men always have access to other channels of information that women don't have.

Can you talk a bit about the alienation you've felt here and the work you've done here?

UMA: My alienation has been the feeling of being a stranger in a strange land. When I said I had the rather silly notion that it would be different, the silliness was that they would be as open-armed about me as I was about them. I was very interested in their lives and their realities. And I thought that they would be interested in my reality. What a surprise. And what a painful shock to find out that they did not give a damn. And I'm not just talking about 'they' out there in our communities. I'm talking about other Black women that are supposed to be my friends and my comrades alongside me. They really weren't interested. And I'm thinking, how can they not be interested? So, that isolation and that invalidation. I wasn't even a figure of curiosity. Some days I was a figure of curiosity, but not with the people I wanted to communicate with. Because in that way, they would have been as 'exotic' to me as I was to them, and in that way, it balances out. But there was not even that desire. So that lack of being interested in me and/or the realities that I could bring to share. That was a very isolating experience.

I spent most of my life being quite close to the sea and having land around me. To live in a city where there's concrete all around – I mean, I grew up in a country where there weren't three million people. So you can imagine, to be here, so that I may be sitting in a flat, or in a room like this, I may not see that many people around me, but psychically I can feel thousands of minds, millions of minds around me. Which is different to my sisters who come from many of the first nations, where there are millions of people. To me, that was an experience that I found hard and didn't even actually recognize, just felt but didn't have the words for it.

There was the battle of coping with the immense level of pollution, that noxious stuff that you can't actually see. I found that difficult, and that is very tiring. And then, the weather. The cold. The weather is terrible, but also it's like, people in London are always surprised at the cold weather. They're never prepared for the cold weather. I can't understand it. Not even the white people. They never, never cope. It's like a surprise. Each year, it's a complete surprise. The shops don't have the clothing, the services in no way cater to it. And so I couldn't really turn to people for advice or think, well, I'll eke out for a good pair of shoes. I couldn't even *find* a good pair of shoes, let alone at a reasonable price. And where is it written that you have to wear grey, blue or black, or brown? There's no reason why warm clothing can't be bright and warm and colourful and stimulating.

And I feel there's no passion. There is no passion in this city. No wonder there is no compassion. And so, I felt a lack of the vital juices of life. What keeps life moving. What was seen as *extremes* of behaviour or emotion. As if someone has deemed there is a correct level and you're going over it and somebody's going, 'Danger! Danger! Warning!' Even among ourselves, you're not supposed to feel – I can see all these signs around me, invisible signs saying, 'Do Not Frolic', 'Ecstasy Is Not Acceptable Here'.

ZHANA: I know what you mean, you'll be coming around a corner and it will hit you suddenly. It's like a wall just sprang up.

UMA: Yeah, and here I'm talking about Black people. It's like, a raised voice is automatically seen as anger. People cannot differentiate between excitement, pain, and the different forms of excitement. There are fine variations in our emotional range. And there is no validation for that. And the thing is, most of the people I see around me, a lot of the time are unhappy, right? So it's like, but they want me to act like them. And I think, why? I'm happy being the way I am. If I saw you having a good time, and I was sat here thinking, 'they're having a good time,' of course I'm gonna want to know how to have a good time. But not when they look unhappy. I don't want to look unhappy. There was nothing in the way they lived their lives that made me want to be like them. And so that was the isolation. And I had very few people to discuss that with. And, in fact, I found, if there was bonding going on on that level, it was actually with Black women who were from elsewhere and often, say for example, from Africa or from Southeast Asia, and we were sort of recent arrivals. Two to three years that we'd been here. And that we were still talking about it. Other people had either adjusted or pushed it to the back of their mind or just thought they'd endure it till they went home, or whatever, found other ways of dealing with it, right? But it was the ones who were within two to three years of being here that were talking it out, and for whom it was a topic of conversation. And also, because we were sharing, we could laugh about it. The silliness of things that happen. And that was nice, that I was able to have that. But that was an isolation.

ZHANA: Can you talk about your work here?

UMA: I have been active primarily around the Black women's movement, specifically in London, although I have gone out of London a little. Yes, all right, maybe to a tiny degree I will accept that Black women here may have had a reason to think, 'Well, who does she think she is? She's coming over here mouthing off about the Black women's movement here.' I've been here three years and I have worked very, very hard. I do not find it acceptable in any way, shape or form that I should be treated as an outsider when I have been a *vital* aspect of the Black women's movement and instrumental in things moving.

I have been active particularly around health and, narrowing it down, around reproductive health and reproductive technology. I have, in fact, not found one other Black woman that's actually active around that. And I would like to do more around that. I have been very involved in creative aspects, and my own creativity has increased in some way. I think it's an aspect of suffering. It's one of the aspects of going through intense painful experiences, that you break through something. And I've also been in situations to develop my own creative self. I have been very much a receiver of people arriving, certainly from my part of the world, and also from other places. I have tried to make where I live available. So I have been networking. And I have also met with women, Black women activists, front-line activists from the first nations, from different parts of the world, in a way that I wouldn't have been able to do. That's been incredibly exciting. Because it's a crossroads. Because when international conferences happen, women pass through here and I've been able to do that. That has been incredibly exciting. For me, to be able to see one piece of Black theatre, entertainment, creative work, in a year is rare. For me to have been here in London, to see so much, that has been just so inspiring. Those sorts of things have been totally inspiring and I have really enjoyed that. Those are the kinds of things I will take back.

I think, in terms of valuable lessons, painful or otherwise, I have seen how power can corrupt us. I have seen how Black women, in fact, worked against Black women. I knew what it was like to be the one Black woman. Now I've seen what happens when there's two of you, what happens when it's half and half, what happens in a collective where there's only one white person. I have seen, also, what happens when you're an all-Black collective. What happens when you're an all-Black-lesbian collective. I have actually seen all those things. I have seen how we ourselves cannot resist power and how we can get intoxicated by it. And I hope that I have learned from that experience. And I hope that that will make me very aware. Because the patterns repeat. And I want to learn from that experience how I have been, how I've felt, and how other people have been treated as well. And so that's been very valuable. I know what signs to watch for. And, yes, I have been challenged. I have been challenged about my attitude, my assumptions, how I see people. But the joyous thing is still, through those immense differences, making the connections. And I am so excited. I want to go to the Caribbean. I want to go to Africa. I want to go to Southeast Asia. I want to go to Black countries. I want to travel through the Indian diaspora. There's all these things I want to do. It's just opened up the world even more for me. And I want to share so much. I want to continue being a link between women in the Pacific and women here. Because what happens when you come here from overseas, particularly Black women who are brought over here by predominantly white groups, they bring you over here as they do anywhere. Local Black women are always invalidated and excluded. Because I've the experience of seeing a rare opportunity where there were twelve or thirteen Black women on a panel on which I was speaking, there was even an Aboriginal woman. Not one of those women was a British-born Black woman. In Australia, the same thing would happen, where you wouldn't see an Aboriginal woman there. So that, local Black women and Black people are invalidated by these people. It also means that, when you're travelling, you're desperate to meet Black people, and the white people actually work towards your not meeting them. And you barely have time. And you look longingly out of car windows, bus windows. Yes, it's nice to go down to the market, etc. But you're not making those connections. Now, because I've been here for that long, I was able to be a door into it. I could take Black women and introduce them, so they could actually speak, sit down and just share. Or, if they didn't want to, just relax. To be in a Black environment. That's what I like to be able to do. So now, when I go back, I know that when my sisters come over here – and of course, I have been involved in raising the awareness and the excitement and the interest of Black women here. Many women have said they would like to travel to my part of the world. And even though it seems impossible, it's so far away and expensive, maybe some of those people will come. And a very valuable contribution will be made, and an exchange will happen. So I've been very much networking and sharing information and disseminating information.

I have found the attitudes of people here in London are very London-centred and they don't even know what someone is doing in a suburb, on the other side of the suburb from them. And there's this sort of half-joking but, unfortunately, very serious and very damaging, attitude of 'Oh, you're a North Londoner. I'm a South Londoner.' And then, no idea of what Black women are doing outside of London. And, in fact, I have found the reception of Black women outside of London to those of us who travel from overseas has been very exciting and they have been more open and interested than women here in London. So, you have to make the links. We're talking about digging back through history for four or five hundred years. (I know we've been here for thousands of years, by the way.) We're talking about Black history that we can document. Now, we're doing that at the same time as forgetting what's happening outside of London, where Black women are being active and part of creating Black history *now*. It's up to us to make sure that those connections happen, and continue doing that. So I've been continuing to network locally and nationally and continuing to be a link internationally.

And I think that's very important. I think that's important in a creative sense, and I think it's important just in the sense of sheer information, on who's using us how. So that we can share that and we can warn each other. And we can learn something from our mistakes and make sure that that doesn't happen.

* * *

ISHA McKENZIE-MAVINGA

Returning home to mother

* * *

Each time you return,
wander home again.
Where love is
Where mother is
Which memories of you will remain?

Each time you return,
eat foods you've known.
Where nourishment is
Where forgiveness is
Refilling with motherlove and home.

Each time you return
to show me you've grown.
you are a woman
you've flown
Your afterbirth slipping from my womb.

Each time you return
just passing through.
I want to mother you again,
wondering this time again
if the world has claimed you.

Each time you return
with the world and its idea of motherhood.
Daughterhood
Womanhood
saying I cannot hang on to your afterbirth.

Zhana – How We Got Here *
CONCLUSION

The move for Black women's spaces is a move for self-determination. Full stop. Self-determination is what we are about. Black women have a history of having our priorities defined by others, by both the empowered and the oppressed, convinced of their right to dictate to us. The perspective derives from a colonialist mentality.

Take one example. In groups of our own, Black women find the space to discuss our sexuality, a marginal subject in male-dominated Black groups. Amos and Parmar pointed out in 'Challenging Imperialist Feminism', *Feminist Review* July 1984, that sexuality is defined by white women in ways that exclude our unique experience. The fact that Black women's sexuality has been systematically devalued by a society which labels all Black women prostitutes or sexually 'loose' has had grave implications for our communities.

Such labelling contributes to many Black families, and especially young Black single mothers, being deemed unfit and disproportionately likely to have their children taken into care. Our groups are also all too often called upon to support Black women who allege that they have been sexually assaulted by the police – the most recent case being that of Jackie Berkley. And Black lesbians who have to cope with soul-destroying homophobia in the wider Black community can often find support in Black women's groups.

Some newly formed projects include a Black women incest survivors' group, a group for Black kids in care, and a Black

*First appeared in *The New Statesman*, November 1985

women's alcoholism group. All of these have been developed on the basis that Black women address our concerns more closely, more accurately and more caringly than anyone else does or could do.

The issues which Black women's groups address may often differ only slightly from the concerns of white women's or male-dominated Black organizations. The difference is that in our own groups we can develop our own political theory in a supportive atmosphere, one in which we do not waste our energy and scarce time arguing over things we consider to be fundamental. Many Black women's groups have made a priority of campaigns against the deportation of women victimized by sexist and racist immigration laws. Although other groups also mobilize around these issues, Black women's support is the fastest to arrive, the furthest reaching, the most comprehensive and the longest lasting, because 'who feels it knows it'.

I have seen white-dominated Left groups arguing over issues which Black women take as given – because our analysis comes, not from abstract theorizing, but from our everyday experience. And while white male leftists who define struggle in Marxist terms feel that their analysis justifies treating issues specific to race and sex as marginal, Black men, because of the severity of their own racial oppression, often feel free to dismiss Black women's separate concerns as irrelevant. So Black women's groups provide a forum in which Black women can confront and challenge Black men's sexism *outside* a context which gives white people ammunition to use against Black men.

Much has been written over the last ten or twelve years criticizing the racism of the white women's movement. I think this is partly because many Black women had put their faith in a movement which purported to represent all women, only to find that we were being exploited and lied to once again, this time by people calling themselves our 'sisters'. Some of the most recent critiques of feminist racism, eg. Amos and Parmar, and Lee and K's 'Womynism' in the *Camden and Islington Black Sisters Newsletter*, March 1985, have been criticized by Black and white women for lambasting the white women's movement without sufficiently pointing the way forward. I disagree with this criticism on two counts.

First, Black women's experience is such that we have every right to criticize racism in the women's movement as well as wherever else we detect it till the cows come home. We have obviously not made enough criticism of feminist racism since we are *still* pointing out instances of it to white women who are no more tired of hearing about it than we are of encountering it each and every day. And second, I feel the way forward has been clearly outlined in both the articles I've cited. To many Black women, the *essence* of our struggle lies in finding, fighting and eliminating racism in every aspect of our lives. Although we resent the amount of time and energy we have to expend in reacting to others' racism, it is surely up to us to determine when this work no longer needs to be done.

One interesting development to come out of Black women's organizing is the analysis of how racism and sexism work together to form a unique oppression. Black women's groups may focus on the fact that Black women's legitimate employment is almost exclusively restricted to domestic work and the nursing profession; or on the marketing of bleaching creams and hair straighteners as Black 'beauty' products; both of which are examples, not only of racism or of sexism, but of how they combine.

Not surprisingly, images of Black women provide a recurrent theme for Black women's groups. Black women talk about our hair ad infinitum. A people who have consistently had few or no positive images of ourselves to use as role models, who have been defined multitudinous times according to how we were seen through others' eyes, Black women are at last coming together to create our own images of ourselves.

Official forms often list categories such as white British and Black African or Asian, leaving out a section for Black British. The implication here is that 'British' automatically means 'white'. Black people, using the same reasoning, often prefer to identify ourselves as Afro-Caribbean or African, finding the term 'Black British' offensive. We choose to perpetuate the distinction between 'Black' and 'British' because we see British culture as having such a negative effect on Black people, both historically and at present. To compound the problem, many Black people who use the term 'Black British' are confused about their cultural identity. They may identify as 'British' because of their identification with their white mothers, rather than because they have forged their own, Black definitions of the term.

Many Black parents are determined that their children will not suffer the same injustices they have undergone. Unfortunately, one parental method of attempting to overcome oppression is still to assimilate, to deny Black culture, languages, and foods, to become more 'British', ie more white.

Over the last several years, Black women's groups, conferences and projects have proliferated, due to large amounts of public funding being made available for this purpose. Although this has led to a dangerous reliance on state funding, it is undeniable that, having at long last been given the chance, Black women image makers are emerging in greater and greater numbers. By recording the experience of Black women in Britain as well as in Africa and the Caribbean, and by prioritizing concerns such as children's books and supplementary schools, we are ensuring that positive Black images are made widely available to children and adults as an alternative to the colonial mentality of Black = 'bad' or Black = 'stay back'.

Black women are participating in exciting exchanges at which we discuss our differences and share our common ground. Although the disagreements and differences have been disheartening and at times counterproductive, they are, perhaps, necessary at this stage in the evolution of Blackwoman consciousness.

Creativity, while powerful and vibrant, is also, paradoxically, terribly fragile. The wrong word or a wrong look at the wrong time can dry up a writer for months or years. Many Black women, including myself, have had the experience of going to a course to learn a skill, be it playwriting, film-making or another creative endeavour, and been devastated by racism from the (inevitably) white instructor. A woman in that situation has several choices – she can either endure the racism in order to learn the skill she wants to acquire, or she can leave, with her dignity intact, but without learning the skills she needs. Or she can, and usually does, choose the third option of attending only as many lectures as her system will tolerate, and supplementing the lectures with her own readings and self-study of Black art forms. Many Black women and men have had to undergo this baptism of fire, and many more will do so, until there are enough Black people who both have the skills we want to learn and are in positions where they are allowed to impart them, until courses are structured in such a way that they meet our needs.

Black British culture is formed out of the experiences of Black people in Britain. It is a rich tapestry, hard to define, enormously diverse. Often, Black people are not even aware of how British they are, or have become, until they travel to Black countries they have previously strongly identified with, and been called 'foreign'.

The Black experience in Britain, Africa, the Caribbean and North America is part of the overall British experience – it is a Black experience that is, undeniably, British. As Black women writers, playwrights, film-makers, actresses, directors, musicians, et al are emerging in greater and greater numbers, recording our images of life in Britain and internationally, it is crucial that we preserve the spaces in which we can share perspectives on the issues that are central to our lives.

*

Resources List

*

This list is by no means comprehensive. It is merely a selection.

Further Reading

Angel, Merle Collins, The Women's Press.
Black Arts in Britain, Kwesi Owusu, Comedia.
'Black Mothers and Daughters – their Roles and Functions in American Society', Gloria I. Joseph in *Common Differences: Conflict in Black and White Feminist Perspectives*, Joseph & Lewis, Doubleday Anchor Press.
Blackwomen Talk Poetry, Choong, Cole-Wilson, Evaristo and Pearce (Eds), Blackwoman Talk.
A Dangerous Knowing: Four Black Women Poets, Burford, Pearse, Nichols and Kay, Sheba Feminist Publishers.
Charting the Journey (anthology), Grewal, Kay, Landor, Lewis and Parmar (Eds), Sheba Feminist Publishers.
The Fat Black Woman's Poems, Grace Nichols, Virago.
Gifts from my Grandmother, Poetry by Meiling Jin, Sheba Feminist Publishers.
The Heart of the Race, Bryan, Dadzie and Scafe, Virago.
Let It Be Told (anthology of essays), Lauretta Ngcobo (Ed), Virago.
Second Class Citizen, Buchi Emecheta, Fontana.
Storms of the Heart, Kwesi Owusu (Ed), Camden Press.
The Threshing Floor, Barbara Burford, Sheba Feminist Publishers.
Touch Mi! Tell Mi!, Poetry by Valerie Bloom, Akira Press.
The Unbelonging, Joan Riley, The Women's Press.
Watchers and Seekers, Merle Collins (Ed), The Women's Press.

Periodicals

Akina Mama Wa Africa Magazine
c/o Akina Mama Wa Africa
Wesley House
4 Wild Court
London WC2

Forward
c/o Africa Centre
38 King Street
London WC2

The Funky Black Women's Journal
PO Box 5
136 Kingsland High Street
London E8 2NS

Maliya (Black women's magazine)
Box No 1
136 Kingsland High Street
London E8 2NS

Race Today Magazine
165 Railton Road
London SE24 01-737 2268
(has also started publishing books)

We Are Here Black Feminist Newsletter
c/o Leicester Women's Centre
94 Belgrave Gate
Leicester LE1 3GR

Bookshops

The Bookplace
Peckham High Street
London SE15

Books Plus
23 Lewisham Way
London SE14

Centerprise
136 Kingsland High St
London E8 2NS

Grass Roots Storefront
71 Golborne Road
London W10 5NP
01-969 0687

Hummingbird Bookshop
136 Grosvenor Rd
Bristol 2

Narada
Brixton Station Road
London SW9

Other Branch Bookshop
12 Gloucester St
Leamington Spa
Warwickshire

Raddle Bookshop and Resource Centre
70 Berners St
Leicester LE2 0AF

Sisterwrite
190 Upper Street
London N1

Black Women's Groups

London

Akina Mama Wa Africa
Wesley House
4 Wild Court
London WC2

Afro-Caribbean Education Project
Women's Action Group
593 High Rd
Leyton
London E10

Black Unity and Freedom Party – Women's Section
c/o Grass Roots Storefront
71 Golborne Road
London W10 5NP
969 0687

Black Women Healers
Wesley House
4 Wild Court
London WC2

Black Women Prisoners' Scheme
141 Stockwell Rd
London SW9 9NP

Camden Black Sisters
Wesley House
4 Wild Court
London WC2

Claudia Jones Organization
103 Stoke Newington Rd
London N16

Deptford Black Women's Group
c/o Deptford Women's Centre
74 Deptford High St
London SE8

East London Black Women's Organization (ELBWO)
c/o Haleem Thomas
285 Romford Rd
London E7

Nigerian Organization of Women (NOW)
Haringey Black Women's Centre
Former Somerset Lower School
Lordship Lane
London N17

Peckham Black Lesbian Group
Peckham Black Women's Centre
69 Bellenden Rd
London SE15

Other Parts of Britain

Abasindi Co-op
Moss Side People's Centre
St Mary's St
Manchester 061-226 6837

Ajani (Girls' and Women's) Centre
3 Mill Hill Lane
Highfields
Leicester 0533-556 796

Asian Women's Centre
13-1-15 Farndale Rd
Benwell
Newcastle NE4 8TX

Birmingham Black Sisters
c/o Victoria Works
7 Frederick St
Birmingham B1 3HE

Blackscribe (Black Women's Writing Group)
111 Burton Rd
Withington
Manchester M20 8HZ

Black Women's Group
Broomspring Centre
Broomspring Lane
Sheffield 10

Northern Black Sisters
c/o Difewan Bookshop
22 Hallfield Rd
Bradford, West Yorkshire

Nottingham Black Women's Group
c/o Ukaidi Centre
Nottingham

Saheli Group
c/o Rasinja Bell
Newcastle Civic Centre
Newcastle

Wolverhampton Black Women's Group
Community Relations
2 Clarence Rd
Clarence St
Wolverhampton W11 4HZ

Community Publishers

The Bookplace
Peckham High Street
London SE15

Centerprise
136 Kingsland High Street
London E8 2NS

Other Resources

Africa Arts Collective
PO Box 129
Liverpool L69 8BU

African Development Agency
135 Clarence Road
London E5 8EE 01-985 0147
(benefits Africans who foster their children privately)

Afro Caribbean Day Centre
8 Fairhazel Gardens
London NW6 3SG
01-328 4311

Afro Caribbean Education Project
Mandel Centre
Green Street
The Meadows
Nottingham

Afro Caribbean Education Resource Centre (ACER)
Wyvil School
Wyvil Road
London SW8
(holds an annual competition for young Black writers)

Afro Caribbean Library Assocation
293 Dalston Lane
London E8 609 9981

Afro Caribbean Organization
335 Grays Inn Road
London WC1

Ahfiwe Saturday School
Dick Sheppard Youth Centre
Tulse Hill
London SW2

Bradford West Indian Parents' Association
17 Claremont
Bradford BV7 1BG

CAPA (organization for Black people's advice and support)
Oxford House
Derbyshire Street
London E2 01-729 1264

Ceddo Film & Video Workshop
South Tottenham Education Training Centre
Braemar
Tottenham
London N15 5EU

Community Librarians
Deptford Library
140 Lewisham Way
London SE14

Feminist Library
Hungerford House
Victoria Embankment
London WC2

Greenwich Action Committee against Racist Attacks
First Floor
78 Sandy Hill Road
Woolwich
London SE18 7AZ 01-855 4343

Greenwich Afro Caribbean Education Resource Unit (GACERU)
17 Beresford Street
London SE18 01-854 2662

Josina Machel Supplementary School
133 Powerscroft Road
London E5 OPY 01-986 5429

Raddle Bookshop-Resource Centre
70 Berners Street
Leicester LE2 0AF
0533-24875

Angela Shaw – Graphic Artist
Gida
36 York Way
London N1 9AB

Unity Theatre
1 Hope Place
Liverpool L1 9BG

The Workshop
81 Lenthal Road
London E8 01-214 6584/254 3082
(a printing and photographic workshop run by five Black women)

International Resources

Association of African Women for Research and Development
BP 11007
CD Annexe
Dakar
Senegal

Black, Migrant & Third World Women
c/o PO Box 29
Fitzroy Vic
3065
Australia

Black Women's Cross-Cultural Studies
Center for Women's Development
Medgar Evers College
City University of New York
1150 Carroll Street
Brooklyn, NY 11225
USA

Black Women's Relationships Project
Dr V. M. Mays
Dept of Psychology
University of California
405 Hilgard Avenue
Los Angeles, CA 90024
USA

Federation of Ghanaian Women
PO Box 6236
Accra North
Ghana

International Network of Black Lesbians
Attn Darnel, NCBLG Officer
930 F Street NW
Suite 514
Washington, DC 20004
USA

National Union of Eritrean Women
BCM Box 7000
London WC1V 6XX

Pacific and Asian Women's Forum
c/o Bangkok Apartment 405
588/3 Petchburi Rd
Bangkok 4
Thailand

Western Aboriginal Legal Service Ltd
c/o PO Box 446
Dubbo
New South Wales
Australia

Notes on the Contributors

Iiola Ashundie

Many people came to Britain from the Caribbean in the Sixties, leaving families behind, to be joined at a later date, like myself, who came to Britain as a young child. As I grew with this country called England, my heart longed to be in the place of my birth. Being transported many mile away, the Caribbean is with me every day as I walk the streets of England.

My writings are based on my own life experience, recollecting those early childhood memories that are still with me.

I am also writing a novel, called *Return to Obyun*. And a second novel is in progress, called *Loving Illusions*.

Debjani Chatterjee

I was born in India, but also spent my early years in Japan, Bangladesh, Hong Kong and Egypt. I work in Sheffield as Principal Community Relations Officer, and am also a writer and cartoonist. As a teenager, I won the Shankar's International Children's Prize for poetry, and in 1988 one of my poems was a winning entry in the Lancaster Literature Festival's national poetry competition. Anthologies containing my poems include: *Watchers and Seekers* (Women's Press), *Black Women Talk Poetry* (Black Womantalk), *What Big Eyes You've Got* (Overdue Books) and *Black and Priceless* (Commonword).

Najma Kazi

I was born in Karachi, Pakistan. I came to Britain in 1963. After leaving school I worked for a year as a laboratory technician at a hospital, before going to London University to study chemistry. Since graduating, I have worked as a food technologist in industry, till January 1987.

I am currently exploring new career possibilities for myself.

I enjoy travelling and aim to see more of the world.

A former member of the *Mukti* Collective, I now work as a freelance journalist, and I am currently co-writing, with Zhana, a book on the history of slavery, colonialism and imperialism.

Lennie St. Luce

Born in Bristol and spending my childhood in Shrewsbury, I grew up in a family of women. I trained as an actress, then worked for several years with the Women's Theatre Group. I have a strong commitment to working with women, expressing and communicating in and through our womanness. I am currently living in Amsterdam, acting and singing in cabaret, and touring my one-woman show.

Zindika S. Macheol

My writing takes many forms, as does my thinking and my lifestyle. Currently, I am trying my hands at scriptwriting and even a novel, which I hope to devote more time to. I grew up in Jamaica and Britain. I still live in Britain but would eventually like to live somewhere else. My aim is to keep on writing and, of course, to continue to play my part in Black women's political and creative development.

Isha McKenzie-Mavinga

Born in 1948, in Birmingham, England, the child of an Afro-Trinidadian father and white Jewish mother of Russian and

Austo-Hungarian descent. I grew up in London, England, in a children's home for Jewish refugees. I later married and then divorced and am now the mother of two daughters and a son.

My life is divided between being a mother, a therapist, a trainer and a writer.

Writing is part of my deep spiritual longing to recapture, identify with and share my Black, mixed-race experience as a woman.

I believe that my father's and mother's spiritual presence has remained with me throughout their material absence.

My survival depends on them guiding me to find the missing parts.

Tod Perkins

I was born in Birmingham during the Second World War. My father, a Trinidadian, married my mother, a Jewess, during the thirties. She bore him four children. The first twelve years I spent growing up in Chislehurst in Kent. Then I went to live in Birmingham again. I was by then an avid reader and used to write long letters to the friends I had left in Kent.

Aged fifteen, I began work in the offices of the Birmingham Co-operative Society, but it was not really my chosen career. Eventually I returned to the South-East and began to train as a nurse in east London.

For twenty years I worked as a nurse in various institutions. I married a Jamaican and had four children. Eight years ago I decided to study for some O-levels and eventually achieved four. I then went on to become a mature student and now hold a degree as a Bachelor of Education. I work as a nursery teacher in an inner-London school. I also write whenever I can: stories for the children in my class and my grandchildren. I am also working on my mother's and grandmother's history.

Judith Kaurmekeli Greenidge

I'm a young Black woman born in Paddington, London in 1964.

I've lived most of my life in Southall, where as a young girl I kept diaries, and it is from there that I began writing short stories and poetry.

Now, at 23 years old, I am happily sharing my life with my lover, who gives me support in my work. I am also working and living in Brixton and am engaged in studying for a Business HND, as I hope to set up my own business eventually and make lots of money. The majority of my writings and poetry I dedicate to my mother, who has given me so much of her strength and understanding. Without her love, I could not be the person I am today. This story, too, is dedicated to her.

Zhana

I was born and grew up in New York City. Four years of study at Wellesley College, a women's college in Massachusetts, gave me the confidence to strike out in new directions. I moved to London in 1982, and since then have been very active in Black women's and community organizations. For two years I taught media studies at a Black supplementary school, because I believe that the education of Black minds, young and old, the images we are fed and feed each other, are of key importance. It is vital that we take on the role of creating these images ourselves.

I am a co-founder of and contributor to the *Funky Black Women's Journal*, and I co-founded the Black Women's Writing and Creativity Workshops, in order to support the development and expression of Black women's creative expression. Having worked for several years as a freelance journalist, I am now writing, in conjunction wth Najma Kazi, a book on the history of colonialism, imperialism and racism. Najma and I are also working together as a research team for television and film, and I am currently writing my first film script. I am moving more towards an interest in creative writing, performing my poetry, and drafting my first novel.

The follow-up to *Sojourn*, provisionally entitled *Sister Sister*, will be an anthology of short stories about Black sister, friend, and lesbian lover relationships. The material for *Sister Sister* will be developed in Black Women's Writing and Creativity Workshops in different parts of Britain. If you would like to contribute to *Sister Sister*, please send an SAE to:

Zhana
c/o *The Funky Black Women's Journal*
PO Box 5
136 Kingsland High Street
London E8 2NS